Cancer,

I Forgive You

SHIRLEY JOHNSON

Paperback ISBN: 978-988-79891-8-9
ePub ISBN: 978-1-952681-73-8
Audible ISBN: 978-1-952681-75-2

Written by Shirley Johnson
Published by Cheeky Kea Printworks
Cover art by Andrea Schmidt, https://www.a-schmidt.com
Edited by Glenys Dreyer

First Edition

DEDICATION

To my son,
Max the Brave,
my hero.

***Love** is the most healing force there is,*
and forgiveness is the way to love.

ADVANCED PRAISES

"This book is a gift to those who might find life is getting worse one way or another. I recommend following the positive tips here to fight adversities! Apply big steps forward, shift mindset, find peace and extra strengths within you to turn negative into positive in life!"
-- Margie S Poon-Edmonson, CEO Paradigm21 Executive Leadership Coaching Academy

"There is nothing as strong as a mother's love for her child! The reader is taken on Max's journey by Shirley who shares her thoughts and feeling and those of her husband in this superbly written inspirational book. You feel the frustration, the pain and the longing to make a difference against all odds. Max is lucky to have such loving parents and older sister."
-- Lind Elsegood, Founder Of LDN Research Trust

"Your child has a brain tumour. What do you do when you first hear the doctor say these words? This book of a family's personal battle with cancer answers this question by following their challenging journey from the initial diagnosis through surgeries, chemotherapy, remission and ongoing rehabilitation.

Shirley talks straight, with openness and honesty. On more than one occasion my eyes welled up with tears. The way she explicitly describes her emotions and what her son went through made me feel like I was there with her. While caring for their son, Shirley and her husband did an immense amount of research into nutrition, diet, and alternative cures for cancer, and all this knowledge has been poured into this wonderful book.

The book also gives mindfulness tips and coping strategies for parents of sick children. If you or someone you know has been given the diagnosis that a child has cancer, this is a book you cannot do without. It's as real as it gets and offers encouragement and hope."

– Rachel Shieff, Life Coach

"On September 18th 2018 my dear mum passed away from cancer on the same day my wife was given the 'all clear' from hers.
Both had suffered all year and my wife had 8 chemo cycles and over 30++ radiology sessions...
In 2019, it was my turn to be diagnosed with cancer which I still have treatment for.... Cancer is a bastard!

It takes courage to face up to cancer and given it has the worst reputation globally, anyone can be forgiven for throwing in the towel. To my mind it's the young with cancer that most bring tears to your eyes for obvious reasons...

For a mother to be able to write a help book at a time like this, is nothing short of courageous and commendable - I am in awe of Shirley's strength!"

- Gary Brightman, Owner of VIBE Book & Music Shop

"This book is about a family's journey of determination, of hope and of the redemptive power of love, the strongest force in the universe. When you are fighting an unimaginable heartache, the shock, pain, and rage can so easily lead to a sense of helplessness and hopelessness. Guilt, resentment and despair, born out of fear, will only destruct and destroy. But goodness, kindness, gratitude, forgiveness and love in abundance will lead to hope, regardless of the circumstances. Love leads to hope, and hope to joy. Max, beautiful boy, we love you immensely."

-Charmaine Kleu, Family of Cancer Patients

"I have never met a more inspiring person than Max the Brave. To see his face light up with that precious smile when he sees me is like seeing the sun come up in the morning - a priceless gift. His determination, his patience, his persistence to keep on trying and his everyday happiness is something we should all aspire to"

-Roberto Astorri, Family of Cancer Patients

CONTENTS

FOREWORD

People around the world have been torn apart by cancer. This loathed disease has likely found you, a family member, a friend or a colleague. In 2014 I myself was devastated by a diagnosis of sarcoma, a rare and malignant form of cancer.

What happens when cancer does the unthinkable, and finds your innocent child. This is the reality Shirley Johnson is dealt with, when her two-year-old son Max is diagnosed with brain cancer, and in the same bewildering day, is rushed off for emergency brain surgery. Shirley learns that when we have everything to lose, we also have everything to gain.

Cancer, I Forgive You is cathartic reading for anyone touched by cancer. It is a stunning story full of the life lessons little Max has taught Shirley.

This book is hope and light through grief. When cancer's shroud first touches you it is encompassing. There is another way. Shirley's journey helps open the door for us all.

Yoki Ilic, *Cancer Survivor, Educator, Mother of Two*

PREFACE

The end of 2019 marked an extremely dark period in history, perhaps the darkest since WWII. Unlike that war which involved only a handful of countries, the COVID pandemic forced every nation to take part. The coronavirus touched everyone's lives: nations went into lockdown, normal lives became disrupted, loved ones were taken away, and some families found themselves being broken up. People were on edge all the time as they fought an enemy that could not be seen. And then, as if all this wasn't bad enough, at exactly the same time, cancer struck my family: my 18-month old son was diagnosed with brain cancer - one of the worst kinds.

Fighting cancer during peaceful times is challenging enough, but adding COVID into the formula was simply unimaginable. I never expected my child to become seriously ill. After all, I breastfed both my daughter and son to gift them the strongest immunity I could through my milk. This was the sole motivation I endured the searing pain in my nipples and the sleepless nights ever since the birth of my first child. I breastfed my daughter until the age of three and she was the healthiest girl I knew; so, naturally, I expected the same thing for her baby brother. Not only was he also breastfed, I kept him at my breasts for much longer than an average mother does for her child. I also took all genetic screening tests there were, to rule out all underlying abnormalities because of my age, in my late 30's, when I was pregnant with him. Besides, it was only fair that I gave birth to perfectly healthy children. It took me years to get pregnant and I'd suffered multiple miscarriages even when I finally conceived. Shouldn't I be given a break? They said that only 1% of expecting mothers would experience recurrent miscarriages: yet I won the freaking jackpot, again.

Fortunately, the depressing years struggling with infertility had led me to find a way to begin my healing journey from childhood trauma, personal demons and chronic condition of my health. Years of training in yoga, meditation and spiritual healing had transformed me inside out. When life dealt me with the hands of both COVID and cancer, I asked myself whether I had what it took to conquer both.

If you are a seasoned meditator like me, treat this book as a 'user's review' on how I applied all the skills, beliefs and affirmations ever since my son was diagnosed with brain cancer. I did not create any new guidance or interpretations that many great spiritual teachers have done, based on some ancient teachings that existed centuries ago, but only on those that have been brought to our attention and elaborated on more during this new age. I would say this book can be regarded as a user review on many teachings we have come across so far: such as the Law of Attraction by Abraham Hicks, Heal Our Body by Louise Hay, and Ho'oponopono by Dr Lew and Dr Joe Vitale. It is a real life experiment on how to apply such skills in a dire situation where no parent would ever want to be in - to have your child facing an incurable illness, a possible lifetime of disability, and all while coping with the COVID pandemic.

However, if you are a novice or have never tried any meditation or healing workshop in your life, I believe you have come across this book for a reason. There is an old saying of "when a student is ready, the teacher is always there." Many great teachers and guides are out there, ready and waiting to guide you when you are ready to embark on your very own healing journey. May this book open that door for you.

The intention of this book is very simple: I would like to help people to see cancer in a different light; to face it with a more gentle attitude. Ever since I joined the club to be a cancer kid parent, I have heard countless times the phrases like "fuck you, cancer" or "I hate you, cancer." Indeed, this was the attitude I held in the early days. Then, even with all the skills I mastered over the years to stay positive and feel good about life, I failed to be the person I always strived to be with my son's condition. Until one day, I had the epiphany about how I needed to forgive cancer to win this battle.

The more I learned about cancer and the available treatments, I was shocked by how stagnant or even backwards the conventional cancer treatments were. It had been decades since the first cancer treatment was discovered. Humankind had landed on the Moon, the Internet appeared, electric cars were born...yet we are still using drugs developed from military weapons during WWII to treat cancer - when cancer patients were used in experiments to test poison like mustard gas, and it was only meant to have temporary relief. The high toxicity had already been established and the drug had been known to kill the body but not cure any disease. Yet, nothing revolutionary has been invented and developed ever since then and today, the majority of cancer patients have few choices other than chemotherapy and radiotherapy, which was as damaging as the former. The immense profit to be made from such drugs draw the world population into a vicious cycle of pharmaceutical companies sponsoring clinical trials and medical research that cover drugs that would bring them profitable returns.

My dream is that there would be conscious in the medical field to develop therapeutic treatments that would strengthen our bodies while turning cancer cells back to normal, healthy ones; or even better, develop vaccines to prevent getting cancer. If the world can pull together in their efforts to develop a vaccine against COVID, an obviously complex and deadly virus, it should not be a dream to achieve similar efforts to eliminate cancer. The Dalaï Lama once said: *"If you think you are too small to make a difference, try sleeping with a mosquito."* This is what motivates me to write this book, not only as a memoir of this spectacular journey I am taking with my son, my family and friends, but also to help readers to make peace with cancer if you or your loved ones are unfortunately in the same boat as us, as well as to raise awareness of what positive cancer treatments should be: NO parents should have to make the decision that we and many other parents have had to: to have to choose between a 'death sentence' or 'life sentence' for our children.

CHAPTER 1

THE BUBBLE HAS BURST

All children love bubbles. Bubbles are purely magical. Merchants monetise from its magic as much as possible. There are numerous forms of bubble making toys these days, even powered with electricity, in order to create the biggest or endless flow of bubbles to entertain the little ones. Each blow is unique; you never know whether you are going to blow some big bubbles or a string of tiny ones. No matter the size or shape, they catch the attention of every single child who stares at them in awe of their beauty, the cocoon of its rainbow colours reflected from the light. Whenever bubbles float in the air, it is as if time has suspended - all eyes enjoy the beauty of the world through the lens created by the bubbles, until they burst.

We held our breaths. I watched the doctor blowing bubbles after bubbles out in front of our son. It was not a usual setting for bubble blowing. We were not in a park nor at the beach. We were in a clinic that was cold and not much of a place for children to play. I watched as the carpeted floor absorbed all the bubbles when they landed. *At least the floor would not be slippery for Max to walk on,* I thought to myself. Nevertheless, Max had not been willing to walk for days now. That was one of the reasons why we had taken him to see many doctors.

***

Max had been lethargic for a few weeks. The first week we thought his body was fighting off some flu bug that had been going around as winter arrived and flu season had begun. Our family received the flu vaccine every year. Weakness and fatigue were common signs that the vaccinated body was defending it from the circulating virus. Despite the usual bounce back within a couple of days, Max continued to feel sleepy most of the time. I took him to see his paediatric doctor who was also the doctor for my four years old. Without fever or any flu symptoms, the doctor assured me that it could be the change of weather that made my 18-month old feel more tired than usual. She asked if he wasn't sleeping as well as he used to at night. In the end, she convinced me that I was probably overreacting. Yet, since Max had a chest infection a couple of months before that had required hospitalisation for several days, I'd thought it was better to be safe than sorry.

A week later, Max was still exhausted. He became unwilling to walk. Before his chest infection, he was able to walk a few steps unassisted. We didn't think much of it as his sister, Jasmine, had also started walking late; she didn't walk on her own until she reached fourteen to fifteen months old. Being bed-bound for nearly a week and losing much weight, we were urged to give him some time to build his muscles back and especially his confidence. After all, Max was still cruising around with his toy walker, at least until that Saturday during the birthday party of Jasmine's school friend, when Max vomited about a couple of hours after he had his lunch. I knew that being sick could be a sign of a brain problem so without hesitation I suggested to my husband, Neil, that we take Max to the A&E of a nearby hospital. But again, the doctor who attended to Max did not find anything wrong with him, either; there was no fever, no runny nose, no coughs, no dilated pupils... all vital signs showed that Max was a healthy young toddler. As it had passed Max's dinner time while we were waiting to be seen, I tried to feed him food that we had brought with us. Surprisingly, he had a good appetite and nearly finished everything, without getting sick. Hence, the doctor was confident that the vomit episode could be a 'one-off' incident, considering that the birthday party was held outdoors in a park and it had been a cold, windy afternoon. For insurance, the doctor wrote us a referral letter in case the vomit happened again, especially without food intake, and we should take Max along with her letter to a hospital further away where there was a paediatric department.

We returned home with a better peace of mind, as if getting a clean bill from the hospital meant something. The peace lasted until 10pm when Max woke up from his sleep and started screaming and rolling around the bed. Max had always been, in contrast to his sister who slept poorly, a dream baby who slept through the night from very early on. So, we thought Max could have had a nightmare resulting from all the drama he'd experienced earlier at the hospital - but he was inconsolable. I pointed out a red flag to Neil that Max kept hitting the lower back of his head as if there was a searing pain. We remembered what the doctor said at the A&E unit earlier, so even though there wasn't another round of vomiting, we packed a go-bag and took the referral letter with us to the A&E of the hospital where Max could be seen by paediatricians.

We went through the same drill as we did earlier. Again, we were regarded as overreacting parents who brought their children to A&E at the first sign of any unusual behaviour. I tried to explain to the two doctors of the night shift how Max was unwilling to walk and seemed to be more tired than usual. As if to humour me, one of the doctors brought a hammer out and proved to me that Max had all the right reflexes.

"Some kids are just slow in gross motor development. Your son's legs have lots of strength in them, he kicked me hard," she chuckled.

To shut me up, they let us stay at Inpatient overnight for observation but told me that they believed everything was alright with my son and we ought to be discharged the next morning.

I barely slept that night. We were only given a piece of very flimsy cotton blanket, and Max's crib was right by the window - so I took off my jacket to cover Max. I was still under the effect of adrenaline, as not only had we ended up staying that night at a hospital, a burglar had also attempted to break into our house. Luckily the burglary was stopped by our reliable alarm system. We didn't lose anything, no one got hurt, and only our door was damaged. I was grateful that my instinct had told me to send my husband home soon after he'd dropped us off at the A&E; I hadn't felt comfortable leaving Jasmine alone with our helper, knowing that if she woke up she would only want mummy or daddy. However, as dawn approached, I could feel a further drop of the temperature in the ward and drafts slipping through the window. I took off my cardigan and added it onto the pile of covers over Max. My body shivered in the plastic chair while counting down to the hour when we could be discharged.

When the morning finally came, I was utterly exhausted. I only managed to close my eyes for half an hour before sunrise. To my pleasant surprise, Max woke up like his usual self again, so I questioned myself whether we actually had overreacted. We had to wait for doctors-on-duty to make his round to the ward again to get him to sign our discharge form.

Max looked disoriented and hungry, and I had nothing to offer him as we left home in such a rush. I reluctantly left him in his crib when the ward assistant assured me she would keep an eye on him. It was still an hour until breakfast was served so I had no choice but to run to the convenience store to get him something to eat. I searched for Peppa Pig, his favourite tv show at the moment, on the YouTube app of my phone. I placed it on his lap and told him that mummy would be back right away.

On the way to get breakfast, I decided to ask the doctors again whether he thought we should have Max's brain checked because I wanted to make sure he was indeed ok, to save us another scarce and hospital run again to have another unpleasant night in the freezing paediatric ward.

The day shift doctor finally showed his face some time after nine o'clock. I retold the same story I'd told the night shift doctors - as if nothing had been put down on Max's clipboard. The doctor asked me about Max's weight and height. He informed me that my son's development was in line with his peers. I felt like an idiot.

Then I pointed at the obvious blue veins showing on Max's forehead. I raised my suspicions that there could be pressure building up inside his brain; I had no idea why though, as the veins were not that apparent just weeks before. The doctor dismissed my question, as if there was indeed any intracranial pressure built up inside my son's brain the veins would be protruding. He guessed it was because Neil was English and my son had inherited his fair skin, which explained the visible veins.

After the ordeal at the hospital, we spent another week hoping everything was fine and that we were just over worrying ourselves. Only towards the weekend, Max spent most of his days napping, despite having full night's sleep. He did not have nightmares anymore but the fatigue really concerned me. I couldn't pinpoint what it was and Googling did not help much either, as it drew similar conclusions to what the five doctors we'd seen told us: the symptoms Max had, did not match with the classic ones that would raise a red flag regarding his brain. Not knowing what to do, I made another appointment with the paediatrician, hoping she could do some further investigation.

We turned up at her clinic again the next day. She was a bit inpatient when she saw us, again; the clinic was busy that day. It was the beginning of December and probably many parents wanted to have a check-up and get some medications for travelling during Christmas holidays. I recounted the events that had happened in the past few weeks, including the night spent at a paediatric ward. She then asked us what more we would like her to do.

"You tell me," I replied.

"I cannot treat your son if there's nothing wrong with him," Dr Yeung said.

I suggested doing some blood work to make sure there was no infection, so Dr Yeung called the liaison lab to have a nurse stop by to draw Max's blood.

It turned out to be a nightmare - needle in, needle out, and again. The nurse could not find the vein. Max was hysterical after being poked and jabbed several times. Failing blood work, I told Dr Yeung to refer us to some specialists who could spend more time with Max to determine whether more tests needed to be done.

Reluctantly, Dr Yeung wrote us two reference letters: one was to a physiotherapist and another to a specialist in child development, since my complaint was that Max was not willing to walk even though he'd started to walk unassisted a while ago. Neil was inclined to book the physiotherapist but after consulting the pamphlet of the child development specialist clinic, instinct told me to make an appointment because there was a neurologist based there, too.

***

Dr Fanny Lam continued to blow bubbles out for another few minutes and we waited for Max's reactions. She had been playing with Max for nearly an hour to assess his condition which, according to the seven doctors he'd seen so far, there's nothing wrong with him. Neil and I watched Dr Lam blowing bubbles out one after another. We did many "ooouu's" and "aahh's", to cheer Max on to catch the bubbles. Nothing. Absolutely no exclamation or reaction from our son whatsoever. Our hearts sank. The comfortable and happy bubbles of our family of four had just burst - we have entered the dark waters of unknowns and fears.

CHAPTER 2

SOMETHING IS NOT RIGHT IN HIS BRAIN

The bubble trick was the big gun Dr Fanny Lam usually pulled out when she wanted to definitely make sure that a child needed further medical investigation, she explained. While she was explaining to us what games she had played with Max in order to access different aspects of his development, I found myself laughing quietly.

Did we just spend HKD4,000 (USD500) to have someone blow bubbles at Max? I thought.

And as Dr Lam spoke, I wondered how come we'd never thought of doing the bubble test with Max.

Dr Lam definitely brought the hammer down to confirm, "Yes, an MRI it is."

A bottle of soaps turned out to work better than a blood test and the assessment by several people with a medical degree? We played blow bubbles all the time with Jasmine and Max, also with their friends whenever we had birthday parties. We'd wasted all this time, and money, to confirm what I had been suspecting - that Max needed to have his brain checked out.

"Something is not right in Max's brain," Dr Lam concluded.

Based on my history of miscarriages and Max's recent chest infection, she suspected that there could be an infection induced inflammation in the brain. As a result, it has probably built up pressure in the brain and would explain the fatigue and inactivity. Dr Lam said she would proceed to arrange to have Max admitted to have several brain scans to confirm. If she was right, the possible treatment was to have IVIG to reduce the inflammation and balance out Max's immune system.

Despite feeling fears creeping up my neck, I sighed with relief that finally a doctor would refer us to have a MRI scan for Max. The treatment did not sound too harsh, either; I had received an IVIG injection myself when a reproductive immunologist found out my over-reactive immune system was to blame for my infertility as well as failures to carry to full term. I'd had several intravenous infusions of donor's plasma throughout the first three trimesters when I carried my daughter. It was uncomfortable but nothing painful - and if that was what Max needed to feel better - I could live with that.

Chapter 3

The 5cm Shock

Dr Lam swiftly arranged for us to have a CT scan and MRI at a private hospital, as the wait would have been too long if we used the public health care system. I did not like my son to be poked and be put under anaesthesia but knew that it had to be done. Max seemed to be half asleep anyway, yet, he suddenly jerked up and fought the nurses fiercely when they tried to set up a needle point on his hand.

It was a long afternoon, and at sunset we expected to get the scan results which would match with what Dr Lam had suspected so that we could arrange the IVIG injection and then be sent home. Only, instead we saw a senior nurse come in with a serious facial expression. In fact, I swore I could see some tears in her eyes.

"I want to come and prepare you first before Dr Liu arrives to talk to you. It's a brain tumour," she said.

My knees buckled and whatever she said to us after that, did not register. If it was not for Neil holding onto me right away, I think I could have passed out.

Dr Liu, who was the neurologist from Dr Lam's clinic came to talk to us. I don't remember the details but I do remember being touched by his compassion and great bedside manner. He told us how sorry he was about the scan and that he had to transfer us to Queen Mary, the largest public hospital in Hong Kong which was also a teaching and research hospital to arrange a surgery.

"What? A surgery?" was the only thing I said to him during the entire conversation. Did he just suggest opening up Max's little head?

"The tumour is about 5 centimetres and is exerting much pressure inside his brain, it needs to be taken out as soon as possible."

Everything that followed after that became a blur.

Max and I were placed on a stretcher and transferred into an ambulance while Neil was asked to get to Queen Mary on his own. The nurse who gave us a preview of what was to come accompanied us to do an official handover to the nurse at the public hospital. I was shocked and focused on soothing Max, who by then was either sleeping or crying for food; we were told not to feed him anything in case more tests needed to be done. He was absolutely starving, having had nothing in his tummy since breakfast. I felt helpless and tried my best to comfort my baby. Suddenly, our chaperone nurse took my hand and gave it a squeeze.

"Don't worry, it's treatable. I've worked at the paediatric intensive ward there before. I've seen cases like Max," then she withdrew her hand and left us alone for the rest of the journey. I was too shocked to respond but was touched by her simple gesture.

Soon we were admitted into the paediatric ward at the Queen Mary Hospital. It was ten-thirty in the evening and I was glad that most patients had turned in for the night. The only child screaming was Max when the nurses tried to replace the needle that had been placed in his vein at the other hospital where we'd had the scans. There was a special procedure room to do this, and parents were not allowed in - they did not want the parents to witness nor intervene when the staff held the child down while locating the vein and inserting the needle. I couldn't bear hearing the screaming of my child. I could hear him crying for mama, daddy and Ja-Ja (his nickname for his sister, Jasmine). Once again, I felt helpless and I wished I could take his place.

I pulled myself away and made a phone call to my father. I had been a very independent woman throughout my life, but at that moment, I felt like a little girl again. I rang my father and told him the news. He asked me to stay put and told me he was on his way.

Then I heard the ward door swing open and in walked a tall man in a biker jacket. I thought he was the father of a patient but dismissed my guess right away. He had to be a doctor as the staff just parted ways for him to breeze through and he headed to the nurse station. He dropped his backpack on the floor and sat on one of the office chairs. I saw him scrolling through some scan images. Could that be the surgeon the nurses told me about? The nurses briefed us that Max should have surgery in the next few days so I did not expect to see the surgeon that night. Obviously, the biker surgeon was not on duty and it looked like he had rushed back as we had only arrived at the hospital ourselves less than 30 minutes earlier.

When I was about to head back to the procedure room to check on Max, a nurse waved me over as the surgeon wanted to talk to us. The biker surgeon introduced himself as Dr Wilson Ho. He pinched his nose where his glasses hung, then spoke with an urgency and pointed at the MRI image that had brought us there. He said the tumour was pressing and generating immense pressure on Max's brain - we could not wait any longer - he was going to operate on him in an hour.

The whole ward seemed to shrink away from around me. I held my breath. I wasn't prepared to send my baby to have his head cut open yet. But before I'd even had a chance to process the situation and ask about the risk, or google about brain surgery on an 18-months old, I was asked to step aside while the team got Max ready for the operation.

Chapter 4

The Shit Show Was About to Get Shittier

I paced around the ward not sure what to do as Max was out of sight when the nurses started the preparation for the operation. Neil had gone to deal with all the paperwork for admission and to give our consent to the surgery. Thankfully, my father appeared at the ward door and looked around for me. I went out right away to give him a hug. My father wasn't the hugging type but I needed one badly after being told my son was going to have a brain surgery. I told my father that Max was being prepped for an operation to take a tumour out. Somehow between our phone conversation and his commute to the hospital he'd made a few calls to doctors he knew. He knew Dr Ho's name and told me that his doctor assured him that the surgeon was the best in the city. I was grateful for him reaching out to get me the assurance. I thanked him for dropping everything to stop by to give me the support and urged him to go home as the surgeon told us the operation would last for six to seven hours.

It seemed too soon that all was ready to get Max into the operation. He was still crying from the needle ordeal and I still kept trying to comfort him while his crib was being transferred by orderlies to the operation theatre. I suddenly struggled to breathe. I knew it was a life and death situation that Max needed to have the tumour out; I also did not need to google to know that it was going to be a long, risky brain surgery. I was reluctant to let go of his tiny hand when we got there and Neil had to peel my hand off our son's.

After the door of the operation theatre closed, it was eerily quiet along the hallway. Suddenly I felt exhausted. It had been a long day. Max had been restless the night before and we'd got up at the crack of dawn to have Jasmine ready for school and Max ready for the assessment with Dr Lam. Living in the countryside meant a long commute to wherever we wanted to be in the city.

I suggested to Neil that we head down to the convenience store to get some coffee - Dr Ho said he would call us when the surgery was over. I didn't know whether or not he expected us to go home and get some down time then head back in the morning - like we were going to do that when our son was having a major surgery.

My stomach had also started to complain about the lack of food since breakfast that morning. I raided the shelf for the healthiest junk food I could find and asked for two cups of black coffee; the coffee was not Starbucks nor Nepresso, but at one o'clock in the morning we took whatever caffeine there was to make it through the next six to seven hours. I held onto my styrofoam cup of coffee as if it was liquid gold. I took in the soothing aroma and the comfort of the heat to warm up my body.

We sat outside the hospital building to get some fresh air because it had been suffocating trapped within the walls of cold clinics and hospitals all day. Neil pulled me in to give me a cuddle. At the touch of his arms all my emotions overwhelmed me. I let go of my guard and allowed the tears to stream down my face. *I was terrified of losing our son.*

Then suddenly Neil pulled me close to him and whispered, "you saved our son's life today."

I could not be more grateful for him to lift me back up when I could not be feeling more down. Later that night, as I paced back and forth along the long corridor outside the operation theatre, I found Neil writing a letter to our son, journaling the day's event to him and telling him how his amazing mother's persistence had saved his life. I took comfort in the thought that he visualised our son living to a much older age to read it.

At about 4 am, my eyes were threatening to close. I leaned onto Neil and the next thing I knew my phone rang. It was about half past six in the morning. I could not recognise the number but slid my screen over to answer it anyway. The man on the phone told me he was the surgeon, and he called to inform us that they had stopped the surgery and Max would be pushed out shortly.

"They said they stopped the surgery, what does that even mean?" I asked Neil. "Shouldn't it be 'finished' or 'completed'?"

Before I could further speculate, we heard the distinct sound of the operation theatre door signal, which made us jump up from our seats. We ran to the entrance and found Dr Ho standing there on his own. He looked very grim and my heart gave a leap. I wanted to ask if Max made it.

When I was about to open my mouth, Dr Ho went on to apologise that he only managed to remove about 70% of the tumour.

"Max was bleeding too much. He has lost about 60% of his blood and we had to abort the operation, otherwise he might not have made it."

He carried on but nothing really registered. I was horrified by the mere thought of what just happened in the operation theatre.

Chapter 5

The 'C' Word

When Max was finally pushed out, I barely recognised my baby, but I knew it was him because he was the only one who'd gone under the knife at that hour of the day, and he seemed to have shrunk after the surgery. There were about a dozen tubes going in and out of his tiny body and because his body was covered, I wasn't entirely sure where the tubes began or ended except for the one sticking out from his head where there was fluid draining out. A net covered his hair and a jelly-like cushion was being used to stabilise the position of his head. Machines that monitored his vital signs lined across his crib. I took inventory of all the machines - first to make sure his heart was still beating, then to check that his blood pressure and oxygen levels were normal. At least he was alive, the rest we could figure out later.

I held his little hand all the way to the paediatric intensive unit. It's the same tiny hand I'd held and the warmth that I'd felt ever since his birth eighteen months ago.

I was still trying to process the last 24 hours - still in the aftershock from his MRI scan. In my half-awake state, I hoped that this was all a nightmare and everything would return to normal when I finally woke up. However, that moment never came.

We were allowed to go into the PICU to see Max briefly, even though he was still out from the general anaesthesia. Then the nurses kindly asked us to go home to take a rest and return during visiting hours. I really did not want to leave Max alone at the hospital but we had to go home to see our daughter, who had no idea what was going on except she had not seen mummy and daddy ever since she came home from school. We also had to bring supplies for Max's stay. The ward would provide milk which would be fed through the nasal tube by the nurses but we still had to get nappies and whatever we thought would make his stay more comfortable.

On our way home, Neil relayed to me what Dr Ho told us, or him. From the extension of Max's bleeding, the preliminary diagnosis of the tumour was malignant but it was still subject to the testing and confirmation from the lab. He also mentioned he had to schedule a second surgery to remove the rest of the tumour. Then Max should be transferred to the Children's Hospital to get chemotherapy.

I gasped at such an absurd idea. Didn't he just tell us that we almost lost him in the first one? There must be some drugs or injection that could make it go away?

Arriving home sweet home, our daughter Jasmine ran to greet us at the door. She was dressed in her school uniform, ready to leave for her K1 class again. It was a déjà vu. We dropped her off at school on our way to Dr Lam's clinic. Only this time, the circumstances were so different that I felt our entire family had forever changed from yesterday's event. At four years of age, Jasmine had so many questions for us. Our helper had told her that we were at the hospital with Max because he was not well. In the end, we explained to her that the doctor found a monster inside her baby brother's head but the doctor took it out last night as she slept. Max had to rest at hospital to recover from the monster fight before he came home to play with her because fighting a monster was lots of hard work!

Telling our daughter using a fighting monster story was fairly easy. However, we wondered how we were going to deliver the news to families and friends. We decided that we would only tell our friends when asked, because we could not stomach the idea of sharing such serious, even depressing news less than ten days before Christmas, especially considering most of our friends were parents.

But with regards to our families, we knew we had no choice but to inform them as soon as possible. Max's grandparents, my in-laws, were scheduled to arrive from the U.K. in two days to spend Christmas and New Year with us. After the initial shock, everyone was very supportive and positive, or tried to be for our sake.

A few days later, we also managed to tell a handful of our friends who were close enough and asked often about our children especially close to holiday time. Yet, no matter how many times I shared the news, I found myself rambling how I'd suspected some brain issues with Max, how many doctors we had taken him to see, finally how one bothered to spend long enough to sign off a MRI scan which led to the horrific discovery of tumour, how the surgery removed it, and Max was likely to get chemo as preventive measure of the tumour coming back. I just went on and on, not once did I manage to utter the 'C' word - that Max had brain cancer.

CHAPTER 6

POSTERIOR FOSSA SYNDROME

When we got back to the ICU, a nurse approached with a grim expression and told me she's very sorry to inform us that they thought Max's arms had been permanently damaged by the brain surgery. I asked her how she could be sure when Max was still sleeping off the anaesthetic used during the surgery?

She told us that the drug would have worn off already. They usually did some tapping tests to check responses from the muscles as it takes a while for brain surgery patients to regain full mobility. She said they received normal reflex responses from his legs, but not his hands, unfortunately.

I looked at the baby lying in the hospital crib, and I found myself asking, *'what have you done to my baby??'* His left eye was completely rolled upward.

Now I could see that he was, indeed, awake and had his eyes open. As soon as he saw us, he made noises but could not really say anything. I looked at the nurse and she confirmed that most patients were mute for weeks after their brains were operated on. Also, Max would not be able to swallow for a while and had to be tube fed; I could see one tube inserted in his nose and taped on his face, and it was just one of the many that hung out of his body. I was going to have to take stock of which was what.

But right now, in front of my eyes, Max was murmuring something and I could see his body jerking. I knew what he was trying to do - he always sucked his thumb whenever he sought comfort. He did that before bed and anytime he felt relaxed, or nervous. When he saw me, he wanted to suck his thumb. He was in a completely foreign environment, not knowing what was going on, so he saw mummy and wanted to suck his thumb, the two most comforting things in his small world. My heart ached for him as I recalled this further shocking news the nurse had just delivered.

Then, the most incredible thing happened. Max kept having jerking movements throughout the day, trying to get his thumb up to his mouth. He tried and failed, tried and failed. At ten minutes to eight o'clock that evening, the hour when we had to leave for the night, Max gave it a big swing with his arm, the very arm that the nurse said appeared to be now disabled, and landed it on his mouth. He couldn't suck it yet given his face was also paralysed and he could not quite move his jaw, nor was he capable of doing any sucking - but he sighed a relief.

My eyes swelled with tears, amazed and impressed by his persistence. That was one of the proud Mama moments I would remember forever. Right there and then, I decided to take photos of him, even in such a condition, because I was hopeful that there would be improvements every day. One day I would be able to show him how brave and resilient he was, and how far he had come along. The images would be shocking to anyone, especially parents, and far different from the photos I had been taking of him up to now. Max was a handsome little baby. We'd received many hand-me-down clothes from our friends. Many of them were Ralph Lauren, gifts from friends and families, as they claimed. Ridiculously, some of them still had the tags on. I enjoyed putting those designer clothes on Max and taking photos of him; he looked like those baby models right out of a catalogue. But now, as Max lay in the crib at ICU, he no longer looked like a catalogue model, but rather a warrior.

I started an album on my smartphone and named it "Max the Brave."

CHAPTER 7

"HO, HO, HO," AT HOSPITAL

We spent both Christmas and New Year at the ICU. But before that, Max had another brain surgery to remove the rest of the tumour that was left behind when Dr Ho had to abort the first one because of the excessive blood loss.

"Can't you let Max rest for a few days to gain his strength back?" I begged him not to open his head up again only two days after he nearly died on the operation table.

"It has to be done. One is because scar tissue may form and make it harder to remove the rest of the mass, and another factor is not to give the tumour any break to regain its strength and proliferate," Dr Ho explained to us.

When Dr Ho came back to get us to sign the consent to the second surgery, we were surprised that he brought along another doctor. He introduced her as the head anaesthetist. They each spoke to us at length, giving us all the time out of their what must be a super hectic schedule to answer all our questions regarding the upcoming surgery.

Neil and I were touched by the kind gesture and their great bedside manner. They both told us how sorry they were that we had to make such a decision, and assured us that they had formed the best of the best team to help Max. It was, no doubt, a very high risk surgery, given the circumstances of the first surgery, yet they also gave us their confidence as this time round they would go in fully prepared: they knew where exactly the tumour was and how it reacted under the knife. Bags of blood would also be standing by should Max require emergency transfusions.

Yet, despite all the reassurance, I felt helpless. How could I send my son in again when I nearly lost him the first time?

In the end, the only thing I felt I could do was to write a 'Thank You' card to the surgery team. I wrote how helpless we were feeling as parents but were very grateful that Max would be in their capable hands. I wished them the best of luck.

I couldn't help myself, but I had to share with them Max's favourite music at that time. For weeks the only thing that would perk him up and got him out of his sleepiness was the Disney's movie 'Moana' - the story about the daughter of an island chief who went against the island rule and set out to sea to retrieve the lost heart of a goddess, and restore the lives and islands that were gradually darken and rotted away. Moana was no princess; she was brave and defied the stereotype of how fairy tales had always portrayed a girl. The soundtrack was very uplifting. They were Max's favourite tunes. I listed the song titles on the card, wishful that in case Max was found in a dire situation again, that the music would help bring him back - just like in the movies.

The second surgery happened the next day. I'd rolled around in bed all that night and sleep never came. The first surgery had happened so quickly fear never had the chance to sink in; but this time round, we knew what was at stake.

Dr Ho had explained to us why Max had lost so much blood during the last surgery and what made the surgery so risky was because the tumour had many blood vessels formed around it. So now, not only I did I know there was a possibility to lose Max, I also feared what another six to seven hours of pressing his face down to operate on the left side of of his brain would do to his left eye which had already rolled all the way to the back, if he made it through.

Once Max was pushed into the operation theatre, I could not stand staying in the hospital. I could hardly breathe feeling the walls closing up. I told Neil that I was going to go for a walk.

As soon as I was out of the hospital building, I found myself jumping into a taxi. I asked the driver to take me to the little town nearby, knowing that I could head back within 10 minutes if I needed to. I wandered around aimlessly; I wanted to feel the normalcy of a mundane life: parents picking children up from morning school, people dining at cafes and restaurants at lunch time, trucks loading and unloading goods....

After what had felt like hours watching the motions and actions in front of me, I checked my watch and noted that it had only been an hour. The surgery might not have even begun yet as it took a while to prepare. Then the barber's pole of a hair salon caught my eye. I found my feet took off and walked in. I looked around the hair salon - there were customers having a haircut, their hair dyed, permed or styled. I needed none of those. In the end, I asked for a hair wash and a blow dry. *At least I got to have my hair cleaned and didn't have to spend a long time on it that I don't have at home drying my long hair, while also killing time of which I have too much of now.* I thought I could use a head massage to take my mind off all the imaginary scenarios that kept playing in a loop in my head. My hair was washed and blown dry - and I'd managed to spend another hour - five to six more to go. Reluctant to return to the hospital yet, I continued with my aimless wandering.

Then my phone rang. It was my sister. She knew Max was having another surgery that day and offered to keep me company after her last meeting at the university she was teaching at. I looked up to see where I was in that little town and spotted the signage of a foot massage parlour. I gave her the address of 'Relax Zone' and asked her to come find me there.

Thus, a foot massage was followed by a hand and shoulder massage later, and I felt much more relaxed - and two more hours had gone by. I bid farewell to my sister who had to head home for her kids. I thanked her for the company; we'd talked about random stuff and nothing about the surgery.

After the much needed distraction I was ready to face reality again. My dear friend Molly, to my surprise, turned up at the hospital. I was touched by her presence and invited her to pace along the hallway with me. She brought me two healing crystal stones which I held onto when I meditated in the meantime. I wasn't a crystal person but I would take any healing power on if it meant Max could make it through this surgery. With the daylight fading outside and darkness beginning to sneak in, it seemed time went by much quicker than during the day, or was it because the company made it much more bearable?

At nearly ten o'clock, the call that we had been waiting for finally came. On one hand, we couldn't wait for the surgery, and hence the worry, to be over; but on the other hand, we knew very well that the longer Max stayed in surgery, the more Dr Ho and his team could do for him.

My heart lightened up when I saw a smile on Dr Ho's face from afar. He told us the surgery had gone very smoothly, with limited blood loss. They managed to complete the operation in a bit under 4 hours. It still took seven hours as there was a delay from the previous operation.

He told us Max was to be transported to have a CT scan to check his intracranial state after being stitched up. Once there, he showed us on the scan image how most of the tumour - 95% to be precise - had been removed. The remaining 5% could be taken care of by chemo.

"It was too close to home", Dr Ho justified the reason why they did not remove that tiny 'carpet' of tumour, as he described it.

We thanked him and his team profusely.

He told us he would be on Christmas holiday in a few days' time and gave us his personal number in case we had any concerns over that period. Again, we were humbled and touched by such a simple gesture. He also introduced us to his colleague Dr Kevin Cheng, another very capable brain surgeon who was passionate about his work, and who also ended up doing the third brain surgery for Max during his stay at the ICU as his brain was unable to drain the intracranial fluid on its own.

***

The Christmas treat we received from the hospital was to allow me to hold Max on Christmas Day - I would never take cuddling my child for granted ever again.

Before his third brain surgery, it was an orchestrated effort and set up in order to keep his head at a certain level to drain any excess fluid out. In order to transfer Max into my arms, that same set up needed to be done again as well as taking the height of my chair and my lap into account. It was a real hassle but it was worth it. It was the first time I was able to hold my baby since we were transported to the hospital by the ambulance. Max knew it, too - even he could not say anything - but he gave us the biggest smile we had not seen for weeks.

Another treat was to let his grandparents, my in-laws, visit him at the ICU. Due to the seriousness of illness in that ward, only parents of patients were usually allowed in. The grandparents' visit was a privilege usually reserved for long term residents, who unfortunately, had to stay for more than a month at the PICU. We had only been there for a quarter of the required time to be eligible for extended family to visit. However, once we explained to the team that Max's grandparents were only with us until the New Year, in the end they were very kind to make an exception for grandma and grandad to see Max. As it turned out, it was the only time they got to see each other for more than a year as the world had soon come to a complete lockdown due to COVID.

CHAPTER 8

THERE IS NO HAPPY ENDING TO AN UNHAPPY JOURNEY

After spending a full month at PICU to recover from the three brain surgeries at the Queen Mary Hospital, Max was transferred to the Children's Hospital. Originally, we had been told that he only needed outpatient visits there to receive a weekly dosage intravenously of a certain chemo drug called Vincristine, for eight weeks. However, upon arriving, we were informed about the pathology of Max's tumour - his tumour was the most aggressive type of which had the poorest prognosis. Our hopes of getting the best prognosis was immediately cut into half. Instead, he required eight cycles of heavy chemotherapy, among which three rounds involved high dose chemo drugs that would take stem cell transplants to rescue him. From the initial eight weeks we were now looking at least a minimum of eight months of intensive and inpatient chemo treatment.

The scenery change from Queen Mary Hospital to the Children's Hospital was surprisingly pleasant. First of all, we were not aware the hospital had only opened several months before. There had not been much media coverage on its opening and I had never heard of any of my friends whose kids had used its facilities. Of course they hadn't - it was a hospital built and reserved for seriously ill young patients who required multidisciplinary medical services, like Max, who needed a prolonged period of chemo treatment and rehabilitation from his brain injury.

Part of the hospital was still under construction and the hospital was understaffed. However, without a doubt, the environment was much cleaner, calmer and delightful because of its colourful and animal-themed decorations. I silently thanked our lucky stars that the timing of its opening was perfect; it was a blessing out of a very unfortunate situation.

I settled Max in his bed which turned out to be an ensuite, an even more welcomed surprise. There were general wards where several patients would share but we had been assigned to our own room for each of our inpatient stays. This was probably due to the high risk of infection which Max turned out to be in after each round of chemo, or because the nurses simply wanted to save other patients and their caretakers from Max's hysterical screaming - a gift that he never ceased giving from his brain surgeries. The ensuite was as nice as one in a private hospital that came with a hefty price tag. The major difference was the pull out single sofa bed that was placed next to each patient's bed for parents which was not available at other public hospitals. At Queen Mary, caretakers were only given a plastic chair, hence it made a huge difference between some rest and no rest at all. I said my gratitude again and hope it was just the beginning of more great things to come.

Looking out at the stunning view from Max's room, there was a giant, luxurious cruise ship anchored not far from the newly built cruise terminal, where the runway of the old Hong Kong Kai Tak Airport used to be. What a brilliant idea to construct something as meaningful as the Children's Hospital and also preserve its heritage to set up a link to the rest of the world, only by sea this time round. The runway of the Kai Tak Airport was notoriously nested among crowded residential buildings. It used to be a test for seasoned pilots for their landing skills. What a fitting metaphor for those who were staying at the hospital built here: *may the flight be smooth and the landing be soft*.

With this fresh start, I pondered what the next year was going to be like for our family, with Max spending most of the year as an inpatient, receiving chemo and recovering from it. We had been told there could be a few days when he could take home leave as his condition allowed in between chemo rounds. Immediately, I knew our annual summer holiday to visit families in the U.K. was gone, but that was not the end of the world as my in-laws were still strong and fit to travel. They'd already planned to return during Easter to see us.

The biggest challenge would be dividing our attention and care between our two children: one being at home with school and the other at a hospital which was a long commute away from home and that also required 24/7 caring from us. The new hospital was still going through a hiring process and it was compulsory to have one caretaker to look after each young patient at all times. Plus, there was no way we were going to leave Max at the hospital by himself without a familiar face around. There and then, I made a decision to make the best out of the situation.

From what I'd gathered so far, chemotherapy was going to be tough for both Max and us. He was too young to receive radiation so the oncologists had the most intensive and harsh chemo protocol to hit the cancer hard.

There was no happy ending from an unhappy journey.

I'd learnt my lesson from my very unhappy fertility journey, prior to the happy ending with the arrival of our daughter. Years of trying and failing led me to forget about the joy in life and I'd promised myself I would never go through the same thing again. Looking at Max however, the feeling was a déjà-vu again. There and then, I made an important and defining decision, because deep in my heart I knew that if I wanted anything good to come out of this, I had to make every day count, to make it a journey of great healing, personal learning, and spiritual awakening.

So, for the first few weeks, I recited these affirmations several times a day and whenever I needed to remain hopeful:

Max is in the good hands of doctors and nurses.
He recovers quickly, comfortably and fully.
We all learn and grow, and become closer as family and friends.
Max will live a long, healthy, happy and fulfilled life.
All is well.

It was no brainer to define my desired outcome: I wanted Max to fully recover from brain cancer, and to live a long and healthy life. And I sneaked in a secondary outcome - I wanted our family to get out of it still being whole. For as long as the journey would take us, I promised myself to still try to live life to the fullest and to have the same for those around me, especially my daughter, to enjoy every single day. I always told people around me that 'Happy Mum Equals Happy Family'.

Therefore, I had one mission - to be happy and stay happy in a very unhappy situation.

BIG STEP 1

DETACHMENT

CHAPTER 9

DO NOT TAKE IT PERSONALLY

You might be shocked by the statement not to take it personally? Yes, my son had a tumour the size of a golf ball in his little 18 months old head and I CHOSE not to take it personal. Why? Not taking it personally allowed myself to focus on him first. It was not a denial. I felt the emotions but at that moment, the emotion that was clear to me was shock, and shock only. If I took it personally, which would be all about me, I could imagine myself crying my heart out. No one would have blamed me: I was a mother whose son was lying paralysed in a hospital bed from three major brain surgeries, who was going to witness poison injected into her son's body, and had no choice but to watch him suffer from their toxicity. However, by not taking it personally, it allowed me to let the emotions come at their own pace. If I focused on my own feelings, my mind would have started to go wild; a movie playing a poor mother whose son was sick then writing its ending and heartbreak on its own. But that was not the reality - it was only imaginations fuelled by emotions then the imaginations created even more similar emotions. I could easily fall into imagining, crying, and imagining more heart-breaking moments to come. I knew I had to stop that fast train before it went out of control and derailed.

On this topic, I have to recommend a TED talk by the Belgian actor Frederick Imbo. He shared his two strategies on *'how to NOT take things personally'* in 2019. It was a wonderful presentation with much humour and wisdom. He told the audience that he worked part-time as a football (or soccer) referee for a pathetic salary of twenty Euros a month. He said he did it to stay fit, and to learn how not to take things personally. A referee was probably the most hated figure at a sports game, so he could never be right: "Are you blind?", "Blow the whistle, not your boyfriend!", "What game are you watching?", "How much did they pay you???" the insults were endless. Indeed, if a referee took on board all whatever the fans yelled at him, he could easily become the most miserable person on the planet. Imbo then went on to use two sides of a coin to explain his two strategies.

One was: '*It's not about ME*'. To do that, we only had to flip the 'ME' to 'WE'. It meant to think in other people's shoes, try to understand where they come from, and thus their actions or reactions. Look at the big picture - the WE PICTURE. The other side of the coin is not hard to guess, and that is '*It's about ME*'. The other party had said or done something that triggered a reaction in me, or the ego in me. We could reflect on the root cause of such a reaction because it often told us there was some truth in it. Then we should step aside and offer ourselves empathy. Our ego would always want to be right - but wouldn't it be easier just trying to be happy? Trying to be right at all times was exhausting. By being empathetic, we allowed ourselves to be vulnerable, to be able to speak up such that our counterpart could understand where WE were coming from.

Imbo' s closing of his presentation was my favourite part. He took out a twenty Euro banknote and asked the audience who would like to have the salary he earned from being a referee. Of course everyone raised his or her hand. Then, step by step, he put the bank note into his mouth, gave it several chews, then spit it out - and that was not all. He then stomped his feet on it. He picked up the banknote, unfolded it, held it up and asked the audience again if anyone would still want to have his twenty Euros. This time round, only a couple of hands were raised. He asked one of them why. That audience member responded, "because it was still twenty euros."

Imbo concluded his speech with this:

"*It does not matter where we are eaten up, spat on, and walked all over, the value within us still remains.*"

It could not be more true.

There are so many great spiritual teachers out there and so many self-help books, more often based on the same old principles but presented in different ways. Sometimes these books are given poor reviews, accusing the author of just copying another author on the same topics. Yet, I saw it as reinforcing those principles with one author explaining better on one while another interprets better on others. Some authors manage to present some complex ideas in simple languages that I was certain could reach a broader audience.

Abraham Hicks, the author of '*Law of Attraction*', in my opinion, was one of the greatest spiritual teachers in modern days. However, I did not think it's easy for any beginner to take on her teachings the first time. It took me a while before I felt ready to listen to her. Why? She could just be speaking in a foreign language. When you have never done any spiritual learning before, you are destined to scratch your head bald trying to figure out what and where the hell the 'Vortex' was, how you could 'tune in, tap in to the Source', or worse, how could I 'get ready to be ready to be ready'. That was the reason why I love learning from various teachers even though I knew in my heart that I had already heard them all. Robin Shama, the author of the book 'The Monk Who Sold his Ferrari', said in one of his inspiring workshops that if we hold an open mind to learn, even the worst seminar would give you some insight; never underestimate the impact of a single take-away.

So, time and again, whenever I found materials that overlapped with each other. I was pleased. It meant another person had found it transformational.

As Abraham Hicks said, "*Words don't teach, only experiences do.*"

In the past half a decade, I studied, applied teachings from various teachers all over the world, and achieved phenomenal personal healing and transformational changes as well as personal growth. I shared the same wisdom with my friends and clients who also enjoyed similar benefits to different extents. With this in mind, I felt confident and had the comfort that I would be able to make it through this encounter with Mr. Cancer.

Every book began with page one, and every journey began with step one. The best first step, in my opinion, was detachment: It was one of the most important learnings from Jay Shetty who wrote the book 'Think Like a Monk'. In other words, do not take things personally. Just like Imbo presented in his TED talk how we could do it by not letting our ego take over. Shetty did a fine job explaining the difference between ego and self-esteem:

Ego does not like other people while self-esteem gets along fine with people.

Ego thinks that it knows everything while self-esteem wants to learn from everyone.

Ego always wants to prove itself, while self-esteem tries to express itself.

Ego takes people's words personally, while self-esteem filters what people say.

Ego compares to others, while self-esteem compares with itself.

Ego wants to be seen as strong, while self-esteem is fine with being vulnerable.

Ego is arrogant, while self-esteem is respectful of others.

Ego inflates ego, while self-esteem builds confidence.

Shobha Nihalnani, an accomplished author and a friend I met through International Coaching Federation, where I received training and qualification as a life coach, wrote one of the best books on the topic of self-esteem. In her book, 'Reboot, Reflect, Revive', Shobha has done a phenomenal job in explaining what self-esteem is and why it is the foundation to psychological health, professional achievement, personal happiness and positive relationships. Quoting from her definition,

'Self-esteem is subjective, and it has been created to refer to the difference between one's current self-image and one's ideal self-image. 'Esteem' is related to 'estimation', so when we compare who we think we are or who we want to be, we are estimating the value of our current self. If the gap between current and ideal self is high, we have estimated our self to be low, so we have low self-esteem. If the gap is narrow, we have higher self-esteem.

For sure, in the coming months, my self-esteem and my ego played games in my mind, the former being the angel and the latter the devil.

BIG STEP 2

CONSUME THE NEGATIVE ENERGY

Consume the negative energy, do not let it consume you.

Emotions are energy in motion. Negative emotions are a force with destructive power. It is important that we recognise, own up to it, and not give the power away. We should not bury the negative emotions, either. Harboured anger could easily turn into resentments, and sadness into depression. Detachment saves us from drowning into the negative emotions we feel and let the forces pull us down into a whirlpool of sorrow. It allows us to acknowledge the negative feelings without giving away its power.

Very often we find ourselves becoming offensive when owning up those negative emotions.

"Are you angry with me?" a husband asks his wife.

"I am not angry..." his wife replied, then stormed off.

Does this sound familiar to you?

To help us to learn whether we are experiencing negative emotions and being affected by them, here are some barometers that can help us to do some quick self-checks:

Do we have a habit of cursing?

Do we easily find ourselves criticising others?

Do we often compare ourselves with friends, families and even acquaintances?

Do we care about what other people say or think about us too much?

Do you often feel you are not doing enough? or simply not feeling good enough for someone and something?

If most of your answers to these questions are 'Yes', then there are major negative emotions stored within you and impacting you, that need to be owned up to, processed, and resolved.

CHAPTER 10

ANGER

Anger is the most common form of negative emotions that affects our everyday life and all our relationships. If we do not process our anger, release the energy, then we become easily irritated by even tiny, trivial matters. The irritations then turn into anger directed towards the people around us. Anger often triggers more anger, then it becomes a vicious cycle and a constant presence in our lives.

Anger? Where do I even begin?

I felt like I had to meditate 24 hours a day in order not to feel angry ALL the time, ever since Max's diagnosis. How about starting with why cancer even existed in the first place? I was angry with the scientists, oncologists, and that pharmaceutical companies still have not figured out a cure in the decades since the first cancer case was confirmed. My blood boiled by simply thinking of how children had to suffer from such horrible diseases. Who would not feel angry when you hear an innocent child gets cancer? And your very own blood? I knew that my husband wanted to punch a wall or beat a bad guy up when we learnt about the MRI scan results. He'd probably only been able to control himself because he wanted to make sure I was alright and there was someone with a clear head to get our son immediate medical attention.

***

I was angry with Max's paediatrician. She had been referred to us by my OB/GYN who I liked very much and delivered my first child. As I had ended up having an emergency caesarean birth, a paediatrician was required to be present, and she came as a package with my gynaecologist. Because we liked and trusted our OB/GYN, we naturally went to the referred paediatrician's clinic for health related matters that concerned our children. Fortunately, we did not need to visit her much as my daughter was very healthy. Besides vaccinations, she did not need any medical attention, which I credited to my breastfeeding for three plus years. But then, my son was sick. Was I angry with myself for not insisting on breastfeeding Max for just as long? To be fair, and to my relief, he weaned himself off at 14 months old - he simply preferred solid food and formula. He was no longer interested in mummy's breasts; he was never crazy about breast milk, like his sister was.

Anyway, we had only seen our paediatric doctor three times before I found Max being tired all the time and becoming reluctant to walk. Since those were the only symptoms he had, as busy as she was with appointments lined up back to back, commuting between hospitals to attend to new-borns or young patients, we were sent home empty-handed each time.

"I don't know how to treat your son, if I do not know what's wrong with him," she'd explained.

She was not wrong though. She had no idea whatsoever was wrong with Max.

Nevertheless, she also refused to spend more time observing him. I suggested whether it could be brain-related, as it was what my mother instincts had told me, but she assured us that was absolutely not on her guess list. He did not display any symptoms that would suggest such a possibility. It was only because I insisted that we would not leave until she referred us to someone who could spend more time with Max that led us to a specialist who finally referred us to a hospital to conduct a number of tests and scans to Max's brain. I know that my husband is still very mad at her to this day, angry at the fact that if we had listened to her, Max could have just slipped away as the tumour grew, and died without having a chance to save him. He swore he would never step into her clinic again, neither would our children.

How about the paediatric ward of the Princess Margaret Hospital where we took Max to spend overnight to have him observed after he had a vomit episode? I explained about the unusual lethargy, wobbly walking or unwillingness to walk - I even pointed at the blue veins that had appeared lately on Max's forehead.

"Can this be caused by pressure inside my baby's head?" I asked the third doctor who came to check on Max since our admission.

They had checked all the vital signs, blood oxygen level, even tapped here and there on both of his legs to confirm everything seemed normal in terms of muscles concerning his gross motor skills.

"Some kids are just a bit late in development," they reasoned.

We were sent home the next morning. By then even I was convinced that I'd overreacted. But, better safe than sorry, and no harm looking stupid, as long as Max was OK.

Only he wasn't. Ten days later he was rushed to another hospital to have his head cut open in order to save his life.

***

How about the senior oncologists at the Children Hospital who had a poor bedside manner? While we were waiting for the pathology report on Max's tumour subtype, we were hoping that it belonged to a group of lower risks. When the oncologist did his round of visits for the day, he casually dropped the bomb on me, as I told him I was hoping that Max only needed three rounds of chemo, instead of eight. He laughed at how naïve I was - that my son's tumour had the worst prognosis.

My husband was outraged that the doctor would just casually make such a statement while he was not there to support me, and the fact that he thought it was funny that I was being hopeful. For me, I was just shocked and was in despair that my hope of having a chance that Max's illness was treatable was taken away from us.

For as long as we were frequenting the Children's Hospital, our oncologists never asked how we were. It was quite the opposite when we consulted with overseas doctors for second opinions - the first questions they usually asked was how we were holding up as parents. Hope was a scarce commodity within the hospital. I had heard from more than one parent that certain oncologists just sent them home to make memories, as the survival rate of their child's diagnosis was close to zero. It was so offensively cruel to rip the hope off a parent, and that pissed me off.

How about the department head of Oncology who told us there was nothing they could do for our son after his chemo, although it was almost certain that he would relapse given the pathology of his tumour subtype? We requested to meet with him when Max's chemotherapy was about to come to an end. As he was too young to have radiation, which was supposed to be the most effective conventional treatment available to kill brain cancer, we wanted to do something once Max was out of treatment. It did not sit right with us knowing the aggressive nature of Max's tumour, that by just treating the symptom, that would be it, and there was nothing else we could do but to wait for a relapse, praying that he would be old enough by then to get radiation treatment. Indeed, that was what the doctors were telling us - that the chemotherapy was only to buy us time until he could be treated with radiotherapy - and even with that, they would be holding their breath.

When Max's chemotherapy was over, I urged to have the port line on Max's chest removed - it had been put in for chemo drugs and various medicines to be administered intravenously. However, as the tube directly connected his blood vessels to the outside world, there was a high risk of infection: blood infection, the worst kind. I'd read from overseas blogs that the port line had a shelf life of about 6 months, then it should be removed or replaced. The caring of the port line was strictly done by nurses at the hospital or by community nurses who did home visits at our house. I asked the doctors when the port line would be removed every time we went back for a check-up. Each time, the doctors replied to leave it there for the convenience of drawing blood. I protested as I believed the risk outweighed the convenience. Max was still vomiting from time to time due to the effect of chemotherapy and brain surgeries. He also had problems regulating his body temperature which resulted in profuse sweating whenever he slept. Combined with humidity, it was like a perfect environment for any bacteria to brew and breed. Besides, Max had a very high pain tolerance and never shied away from needles. Yet, I was dismissed every single time.

Five months after the completion of treatment, Max suffered severe abdominal pain and developed a fever. We took him to the hospital and they did a blood check on him and immediately put him on antibiotics, but it did little to bring down the amount of bacteria found in his blood. On the contrary, the type and amount of bacteria alarmed the microbiologists based at the Children's Hospital. The microbiologist suspected that the port line was the culprit, which turned out she was right. They performed an urgent operation to remove Max's port line and confirmed what they had suspected - what had caused Max's serious septic infection was the port line being full of bacteria, and the most dangerous ones. Max suffered a great deal from it and had to be on very strong intravenous antibiotics round the clock for two weeks. He lost a lot of weight while his body went through waves of vomits and diarrhoea while the antibiotics were doing their job to get rid of the bacteria.

I was beyond furious and could not help myself and said, "I told you so," to his oncologist.

Shockingly, the oncologist turned the table around and accused us of not taking good care of the port line, which was ironic when caretakers were forbidden to touch it. Unlike in other countries, saline solution and needles were prescribed to patients such that their caretakers could do the caring and maintenance of the port line at home.

***

The nurses. There were a handful of wonderful, compassionate nurses at the Children's Hospital who had been more than helpful to us, but that was it. They were like the few good apples among a full basket of bad ones and I sometimes feared that one day they too would turn to rude, unsympathetic nurses that formed the majority of the nursing workforce at the hospital. I wondered whether it was because the Children's Hospital was a new one and was kind of located in the middle of nowhere.

During our time spent there, we had seen quite a few career movements, most moving to other public hospitals. I once asked why on earth anyone would rather work in a crazy, busy, less than pleasant environment than a rather new, peaceful and beautiful hospital? I did get my answer: the other older, more established hospitals look much better on their resume. As this hospital was new, the hiring was in phases. Despite a lighter workload, each nurse was looking after a larger number of patients. However, from the long period of time we had resided at the hospital, I could tell that the nurses there were merely distributing medicine, administering chemo drugs and preparing intravenous nutritional feedings. The actual caring was all done by parents or caretakers. It was compulsory to have one caretaker by each child patient 24/7.

The nurses all seemed to be super busy but when we reflected to the doctors that it was very overwhelming to be caring for a sick child as one person, the doctors asked why we did not seek help from the nurses.

"They hardly have anything to do!" they'd say.

"They are too busy creating problems for us parents," I jokingly replied. "We've been told not to bring food from home to feed Max, for safety reasons, to prevent food poisoning. I understand the rationale behind it as children receiving chemotherapy were immunocompromised."

Then I asked what we could do as the meals serving time were way far apart from Max's routine. They said the only thing allowed was to microwave the served meals.

"Who is going to watch my son when I go to the kitchen to join the queue to warm up the food?"

"We will, just come and find us," the nurses told me.

I never asked for their help again after asking twice and both times coming back to find no one in the ward except Max, crying for his mama, while struggling to climb out of his highchair.

All the headaches and arguments we had with the nurses, nearly on a daily basis, originated from one fundamental mentality: one size fits all. Despite the hospital catering to children from 0 to 18 years old, the same treatments applied to all, i.e. what you see is what you get.

However, every child is different and has unique needs. For example, my son slept on his tummy. He had to be on an IV the whole time he was an inpatient and the line wasn't long enough for him to sleep in the crib while having the safety gate pulled up all the way. I raised this issue to different nurses including the ward manager, that the IV tube was not long enough and each time the answer I received was 'it's the same for everyone'.

I was not too concerned about this during the first few cycles of chemotherapy, as Max had suffered from severe Posterior Fossa Syndrome - he was paralysed from neck down after the two major brain surgeries to remove the tumour. Week after week, I was thrilled with the progress he made with his movements, but simultaneously my concern with the safety of the crib grew. When we checked in for the fifth cycle, I raised my worry and asked for a longer IV tube again. I even invited the IC, nurse-in-charge, to come and see how the safety gate could only be closed to the second highest level.

"Nothing we can do. Watch your baby closely," she said with a shrug.

There was nowhere else to put my baby when I needed to go to the toilet, especially at night when I had to step away.

"Can we have two people here?" I asked.

"No, it's the same for everyone, one caretaker only," would always be their reply.

As it just so happened, it was during this fifth cycle that Max surprised his mummy with his improved mobility - he climbed out of the crib! I had only stepped away for merely five seconds to replenish the nappy stack I piled at the end of his crib and during that brief moment, he managed to climb out and landed on his head from a height of about 1.5 metres. As if the nurses knew the implications, no one mentioned anything about the tube; they actually blamed it on me being careless and not watching closely enough.

Of course, no one felt worse than I did, Max did fall under my watch. After all, his skull had become more fragile from the drilling during a surgery to create a balance of his intracranial pressure. We spent a week of worries and anxiety, holding our breath every time we had a scan to make sure there was no internal bleeding. Finally, after the week had passed I felt more relaxed that no internal and permanent damage had been done

I then went to seek help from the nurses. I asked whether they could give my son the injection to stimulate urination earlier in the late afternoon or early evening, instead of in the middle of the night. I told them that Max had no problem urinating during the night, and less output during the afternoon, so I felt the best time to give him the injection should be day time.

"But we calculate the output from midday," was their response.

"Oh, then that's easy, you just need to calculate from midnight then," I suggested.

When the nurse calculated the urine output from midday, it appeared that Max did not pass out much urine in the afternoon naturally. The total output seemed low and they had to give him a stimulant, and so, together with his usual urine volume, it then overflowed even a night time nappy volume every two hours. This seriously upset both Max's and my sleep. I am not a superwoman, and I cannot stay up all night to change nappies, change the bed sheets and pyjamas, comfort my toddler who got woken up about ten times during the night, and function fully the next day. I tried to reason with the nurses and have their understanding, if not sympathy.

"It's the same for everyone," they insisted. Why did I even expect a different answer?

My anger towards the nurses gradually turned into frustration. I was torn between being Max's only advocate to his well-being and the nurses' 'one single policy for all'. I tried my best to avoid conflicts by doing more, asking less and expressing my dissatisfaction by placing complaints to the Patient Relationship Officer. However, after a while, I realised she acted as an ear and mouthpiece to pass on the message that there was an official, standardised reply to every issue or complaint - in short, nothing changed and none would. Still, I saw her as my little shrink or outlet when I tried to avoid direct conflict with the nurses. It was cathartic to rant about the nurses or the system which made them behave so.

Despite this, trying to do it all by myself still proved to be a struggle. Caring for a toddler in a non-childproof environment meant we had to bring half of the house with us. I asked the nurses whether it was possible to provide us with a high chair, a baby bath and some protective cushion for the crib (one of the side effects from the brain surgeries was the night terrors he experienced during sleep that would cause him to flap around like a salmon). The nurses looked at me like I was asking them to serve caviar in Max's next meal. So, each admission was like a relocation. We had so many things to bring. Even toys were essentials as the days were long. I had to entertain a two-years' old who was not interested in an iPad yet, plus there were considerations about his rehabilitation. Every toy became a play therapeutic means.

We spent on average two and a half weeks, if not longer, out of each month at the hospital. Yet, we only had an hour of notice when nurses informed us we could go home for a break. We were told that it was a 'home leave' as we were expected to return in two days. I noticed that other patients who were on 'home leave' still had their belongings lying around, so when I pushed Max in a stroller and an overnight bag out of the ward, a nurse stopped me and asked me if I had cleared the bed.

"I thought it's a home leave," I said, confused. "It's late now, and you just came in half an hour ago to give my son medicine and saw his room full of stuff after weeks of stay and you didn't say anything?"

After this fiasco, I asked if they could at least provide us with a high chair, then we would have at least one fewer big piece of furniture to bring along.

The nurse pointed at some kid's chair and table and said, "that's the kid furniture we have."

But I knew my son could hardly hold himself up, so it would be dangerous to let him sit in those. Even when dining at a restaurant for one hour we were offered a high chair, so I didn't think it was too much to ask, especially at a hospital that was built for children, who displayed its spirit in the hospital lobby as patient-oriented.

"It's the same for everyone."

Such a reply had become an official answer to nearly everything I asked.

***

Dieticians: the dieticians at the hospital. Seriously, I could give better dietary advice than they do. All along the single dietary advice we were given was 'make it safe.' Boiled food, processed and packaged food were best, in order to prevent infection as your son's immune system would become non-existent. I looked at the pamphlet that was given to us as the food guidelines, and the dietician was simply repeating what was printed on it. I asked her about detoxing, as I thought about the poisons going into Max's system - I just wanted the chemo drug to go in, do its job, and get the hell out. How about strengthening his weakened body after his treatment? I knew that at the hospital they only dealt with the symptom, so I was concerned what was going to happen once it stopped. The natural countermeasure to think of was to strengthen Max's body so it was less likely that he relapsed. And God forbid if he did, he would be at a better position to fight it.

For example, a cancer patient's bone resembles that of a 90-year old woman after going through chemotherapy. Cancer patients also needed to maintain a much higher level of Vitamin D in their blood to protect them against a spectrum of viral or bacterial infections. Chemo caused so much collateral damage while aiming its bullets at the cancer.

Well, I soon realised there were only two dieticians in the whole hospital and their main role was to advise the amount of milk or fluid to be fed to patients who needed tube feeding, and to be on top of what was being served by the catering team. Hence, the biggest favour we could ask from her was to have some variations in Max's menu. Apparently, however, you could only have one choice in the computer system at a time. So once or twice a week we had to ask her to kindly change the food served to Max. Feeding a sick child was challenging enough, but feeding bland food that looked horrible and tasted even worse made child-caring unbearable. Yet, we were not allowed to bring our own food, obviously for safety reasons. I dreaded the many such meals I had to feed my son from day one.

***

And then COVID. I am sure you readers would cheer me on this one. COVID sucked and dealing with both cancer and COVID at the same time sucked multiple times. Did I mention chemo rip you off all neutrophils? That made my son, contrary to kids who rarely caught the virus or would not have it as bad, a primary target, and if the cancer did not kill him, COVID would have finished the job. Due to COVID, no charity personnel were allowed into the ward. It meant no play therapies were offered to kids who would spend days there, if not weeks, every time they checked into the hospital. No visits were allowed, either. No families or friends were allowed to come give some much needed hugs and love to us. And only one caretaker was permitted at a time.

'It takes a village to raise a child.' What follows should be, 'and it takes an army to care for a sick one.'

Nurses in the ward would only care for the medical sides of the patients. They distributed medicine, delivered the IV fluids and made sure the right poison in the right amount was hooked up. I saw them as 'the drug dealers'. They were not involved in nor gave us a hand when we needed one.

And they had this stupid and unreasonable policy that you had to swap outside the ward: "One out, then one in," the security guard warned us, with her arms on hips.

I pretty much stormed in to talk to the ward manager. I asked her how long the nurses had when they exchanged shifts.

"One hour," she replied.

"Then fifteen minutes is not too much to ask when I have to swap with Daddy."

The ward manager mumbled something inaudible. So I asked her again whether they would be responsible if our toddler son was hurt during the time we were doing the swap and no one was available to attend to him.

She finally agreed, albeit reluctantly. Yet, somehow it was not relayed to the security guard, so every day we had the same discussion until I made a memo, pinned it at the entrance, and dared anyone who had it removed.

COVID made everyone on edge - the nurses in particular. One time when we were allowed to go home, I packed up everything and vacated the room for the ward assistants to clean up for the next occupant. I pushed Max out of the room in his stroller, from which he had not stepped out of for over two weeks, thanks to COVID.

A nurse asked us to wait for the discharge paperwork, telling us she just needed to wait for the doctor who was on-duty to sign. After waiting for an hour in the hallway, the paperwork was still pending. I tried to be patient and found a chair to sit on.

"Don't sit down, we will have to sanitise it after you!" I was quickly told.

So I was made to stand in the hallway and my son strapped in his stroller for another two hours. After waiting for three hours, I told the nurse that we're going, nothing could stop us, she could call me when the documents were signed. I had to bring Max home for lunch. In the end, it was another four hours later - seven hours from when we left the ward - when they finally called me to tell me that the discharge papers were signed. When I asked around about whether there were emergencies that day, there was none, it was just a regular day. The oncologist on duty went on with his day and a lunch break as usual, ignoring there was a toddler waiting to leave to spend a couple of days at home before another round of chemotherapy would begin.

Max had to have a COVID test every time we went back for more treatment. Without any doubt, it was a distressful test, especially for a barely two-plus year old who had no idea what was going on, why a stranger covered with plastic from head to toe would put something long and deep up inside his nose until tears ran down his cringed face. Yet, no one even tried to be gentle with these kids nor bothered to play some tricks to lighten the whole act up. Even on days when Max would scream, the nurse still forcefully carried out the test because she was already gowned up.

"It's the same for every kid," the nurse reassured me.

***

I was even angry with Max: my poor two-year old who was fighting for his life. My sleep-deprived self was not that loving and patient, I suppose. I had never seen vomit on that scale. There had been lots of milk puke during the early months of their baby days of my two children, yet I wasn't prepared for the kind of sickness that was induced by chemo drugs. I felt like there was a puke fountain in front of me that would catch me by surprise when I least expected it.

I tried to communicate with Max, using my body language, gesturing wildly while holding a bucket, hoping that he would understand and give his poor mum a much needed sign such that I could catch his puke. Many times I felt so helpless when I saw him sitting in a pool of his own puke - I did not know where to start the clean-up.

By instinct, I changed him out of his hospital pyjamas that were soaked to his skin first, since pneumonia was one of the top complications that could kill cancer patients, ironically not from the cancer itself. Even that was a big challenge. Max was feeling nauseous, he just wanted to lean onto mummy, and not be cleaned and have all his limbs pulled in and out of clothes. When I finally managed to clean him, I realised there was nowhere that was not contaminated with his vomit to put him down. I had to carry him while changing the bed sheets and cleaning the floor. I was exhausted and deflated that he had thrown up everything I'd just spent over an hour playing tricks to get him eat. I gave myself a shake and tried to get him hydrated or put something into his tummy again. And, just when I thought he had emptied everything out, here we went again. Where did all this liquid come from? I felt I had nothing left inside me at the end of the day after Max had been sick seven or eight times. I tried to get help, I did. Yet, very often after I rang the assistance-seeking bell, it would still be an hour later before someone would come and check on us. Sometimes the most help that would be extended to me was to bring over clean clothes or sheets. Just looking at the medical staff's faces, it was all in their eyes and disgusted facial expressions: 'your son's puke, your shit to clean.' I got it, I just could not do it all by myself, over and over again.

Woah, it felt good just to get it all out. Once I could not stop myself but I told one of the nurses off.

"You are lucky that you are only helping the parents of sick children, but not their parents!"

The statement shocked me. I knew that deep down it all came down to one thing - one thing that made me mad at the whole world: Fuck you, cancer, for knocking on my door without a bloody invitation. I fucking hate you.

CHAPTER 11

RESENTMENT

The definition of resentment in dictionaries is: *'bitter indignation at having been treated unfairly'.*

By its definition, it is almost only fair for those who have been themselves, or whose loved one has been struck by cancer, to feel resentful towards life itself. And when this resentment cannot be resolved, it will then spread outwards widely and rapidly like the cancer cells.

Many parents go onto social media to rant to strangers, who they claim would understand, because they were in the 'same boat', and complain about their families and friends for doing or not doing this or that. Or they complain they could not get this or that at a shop, restaurant or from certain organisations. However, if you take the context out of the situation, there is no wrong-doing by any of the accused parties. Yet, we felt resentful towards people, especially those who were immediately around us, because they were not 'in the same boat'. I myself was also guilty of this when I asked for, or hoped for, getting some special treatments because Max had cancer; hence, I reasoned, it was only fair if we were compensated with something extra.

Resentment could also be directed towards someone who suffered the same situation. I have heard, as well as witnessed, how cancer had broken marriages and torn families apart. No wonder some parents also described cancer as the 'home wrecker'. Cancer treatment was usually long and financially draining. Even in the best case scenarios when the medical treatments were covered by insurances or subsidised by governments, not being able to work, or in the parents' case needed to be the caretakers for their sick child, many have to give up their jobs or even careers that they had spent a long time building. All these scenarios created enough resentment on their own.

Sometimes, one parent also resented the other because they felt the unfairness in the division of labour between them. When medical treatments were only available far away from home, parents were forced to split the roles between themselves; one to look after the sick child, while the other worked and cared for the other siblings. It was in no certain terms clear who had the heavier task but it was easy to imagine and believe the other got the better deal, and felt resentful over it - when out of sight, out of love. Couples also found themselves growing apart being physically apart for months, as the treatment required. All these tragic developments brought a freshened round of resentment towards cancer and life itself.

CHAPTER 12

FEAR

Fear does not take away death, it only takes away life.
– Buddha

The close call during Max's first brain surgery had generated much fear in me. We only learnt about it AFTER the surgery when he had made it. Without witnessing what actually happened, I could not help but imagine the scenes many times over in my mind: Max's little body lying lifeless on the operation table with his brain cut open, blood dripping through his brain tissues and spilling out onto the surroundings, his heart rate then dropping to the point that the beating hardly registered on the monitor, and then the anaesthetists calling for the operation to abort. A series of motions then appear across the movie screen: resuscitation, blood transfusions, stitching up Max's head... until finally the heartbeat monitor begins to give a subtle more regular beeping sound.

The pictures played in my head in loops and were enough to create such a fear within me that I struggled to breathe and had nightmares about it for a while. That was, until I trained my mind to stop playing that horror movie in my head, and I kept reminding myself with the affirmation that 'Max is fine, he is safe, all is well.' Gradually the panic attacks came less frequently, then eventually stopped.

Even after Max survived one of the hardest chemotherapy regimens for his age and his scan was clear, the fear of recurrence engulfed Neil and I to no end. We were often reminded by our oncologists that Max had the worst prognosis of Medulloblastoma. Among parents of cancer kids, there was a term called 'Scanxiety'. It referred to the anxiety generated from the fear of what the scan would show. While hoping for NED, (No Evidence of Disease), parents could not help but FEAR the scan would show otherwise - because it could mean another long and harsh journey of treatments or clinical trials, or simply the beginning of the end.

Witnessing the passing of his fellow toddler patient who finished the same treatment, just a month before Max did, relapsed two months afterwards and passed away within three weeks, did not help but skyrocketed our fear. As a result, we struggled to relax even when he was finally home for good. We tensed up to his every sneeze, cough, puke, or even just taking a nap. Could this be a sign of relapse? Was he lethargic or did he just need a nap from hours of playing like any child of his age? I realised that going at this rate, we would never be able to live our life to the full, but instead in constant fear.

'Fear does not change the future but only robs the precious moments of today.' It's a quote from my favourite teacher, the late Louise Hay, who I saw as a grandmother who I never met in person nor had but whose voice warmed my heart in the morning and night, as I listened to her recorded audio guided meditations and workshop recordings. I carried this line in my heart throughout the initial months of Max's treatments, especially whenever the thoughts and doubts of 'what if' began to come crawling into the back of my mind. I also have a card the size of a business card stuck on my desk - I don't even remember when and where I acquired it, but I always keep it somewhere I can see it easily because of what it says.

There are two ways to break down and react to the word FEAR:

Forget Everything and Run
OR
Face Everything and Rise

The first option was out of the question. Forget about the situation and run meant hanging Max out to dry. We were all he had. So it left us with the other option; face everything and rise. We did face the situation head on, but how could we rise from it? And how high could we rise?

CHAPTER 13

GUILT

It does not matter how you get here, but how you are going to get from here to there.
- Abraham Hicks

Guilt is a bitch. Any parent would understand this statement very well, and quite certainly would agree with me.

I've lost count of the number of times have I asked myself these questions: What did I do wrong? What did I miss that would have shown the very first sign of that tumour budding in my son's little head? Why didn't I spend my every waking moment to look after him and protect him - then nothing horrible like cancer could have reached him? What if... the questions were endless. My husband, worried that I would be consumed with guilt, kept reminding me that I was the one who saved our son. He reminded me that I was the one who insisted on finding a doctor who would agree to send our son for an MRI. I was the one who suspected there was something seriously wrong, and his brain was the area of concern.

I have heard so many parents say they wish they could swap places with their sick kids. They wish they were the ones who had cancer, who had to be poked with needles numerous times a day, who felt the nauseating sensations whether or not having food in their stomachs. They wished they were the ones who got the radiation, who had to be infected with chemical poisons in the name of a therapy.

This is their guilt talking. This is their urge to punish themselves for not being able to stop cancer happening to their children talking. However, if you consume yourself with guilt, you are punishing yourself and nothing but sorrow comes out of it. When you can let go of that guilt, you will be able to learn the lesson and finally move on.

I managed not to drown myself in tears and focused my energy on Max's recovery and his following treatment after his brain surgeries, until I witnessed the full blown side effects on my little guy after the first round of chemo drugs had been administered.

. Chemo drugs did not target cancer cells - they were simply toxic chemicals to go inside a cancer patient. They killed any cells that proliferated quickly - that covered cancerous cells, as well as healthy cells such as hair and skin. That is why people who are on chemo suffer hair loss. But we all knew that because that's how cancer patients look like in movies. What we may not know is the mucous membranes that lines from our mouth along the digestive tract down to the anus also suffer from the same fate. Mucositis is a very painful inflammation that patients undergoing chemotherapy have to endure.

Our oncologist briefed us on a number of side effects, like a drop in white blood cells, a weakened immune system, and ulcers, when we signed the consent for Max's chemotherapy treatment. We knew we had to be cautious with hygiene and personal health such that we did not expose Max to risks of infections. However, no one had explained to us what exactly 'ulcers' meant in the cancer world.

We have all had ulcers every now and then, but we were not briefed what kind of symptoms we had to look out for. With Max's speech impaired from his brain surgeries, he could hardly communicate nor express himself. So, after Max's chemo drug days were over, I was over the moon to be able to finally take him home. He had already stayed at the hospital for more than a month since the night we brought him in to have the emergency surgery.

Unfortunately, but expectedly, we had to rush him back to the Children's Hospital two days later because of neutropenia fever. We were yet to find out whether he had infections while waiting for the lab to run a number of tests. But Max was miserable. He would not eat, and could not sleep. He only wanted to lie on my chest.

And his hair was falling out. I spent hours every day just clearing hair from his pillow and our clothes. He also started to drool. The nurses did not mention anything when they brought the medicine in, and I had not thought much of it as Max had had difficulties swallowing after his brain surgeries.

But, three days later, the on-duty oncologist noticed Max drooling and he casually mentioned, "Oh, he's in pain, let's put him on morphine."

"What?!" I responded. "Why do we have to give him morphine? Can't he have painkillers?"

The doctor said that painkillers would not do much for that kind of pain. The mucositis caused so much pain that Max could not even swallow his own drool.

The nurses were then instructed to put him on intravenous nutritional fluid, as the doctor believed his guts had also suffered the same fate and that nothing would have been absorbed properly. In truth, Max had suffered bad diarrhoea for days. His bum was so raw that no bottom cream would heal it; I saw yellow pus when I changed his nappies.

I was shocked. I had absolutely no idea my son was in such a great deal of pain, that he had to be put on morphine 24/7 to relieve it. I felt so guilty for not being able to spot it earlier.

Yet, there was no way I could have known until someone pointed it out to me. I knew that Max was not feeling well and he spent a long time just wanting mummy to hold him. So, I let the guilt stay with me for half a day then I decided that's enough. I promised myself and my son that I would do something so that with the next round of chemotherapy he would not have to suffer like this again. The guilt in me fuelled me to do something so that I would never see my son suffer from such pain again.

Because I did not let the guilt consume and punish me, I used that energy to ask around and do research. I found that in the US, there was some drink you could take to line a protective layer along the digestive tract to protect it from the attack of chemo. It was also FDA approved. My husband placed the order and took care of the logistics to make sure it would arrive in time for Max's next round of chemotherapy. Max has never suffered serious mucositis ever since.

CHAPTER 14

DOUBT

How many times do parents doubt themselves? I bet the answer would be all the time.

When it comes to parenting, our children did not arrive with a manual on how to raise them. There's no built-in error codes telling you what's wrong, when something is wrong, or simply if it's a false alarm. Definitely no to-do and not-to-do list when your child has a serious illness. You question yourself often, 'am I doing the right thing for my child?' 'Am I going to regret making such a decision?' 'Will he or she blame me one day for compromising his/her quality of life just to keep him/her alive?' The questions are endless and there are no right or wrong answers. We can only rely on the information available out there - other people's experiences - and finally trusting what your guts tell you that's the best decision to be made at that particular time and situation.

Our biggest doubt to date during Max's cancer journey was whether to subject him to radiotherapy. Everyone said radiation would be the most effective treatment to kill the cancer, especially given the pathology of his tumour subtype that has the poorest prognosis, with only a 20% survival rate versus the best subtype over 90%.

No doubt, you should radiate your son's brain and spine if you want him to live past his childhood years. Then what? To have my son stay forever as a two years old? What kind of life will we be offering him? He would never be able to take care of himself independently. We would be robbing him off stages of life every other child gets to enjoy, falling in love, having heartbreaks, getting married, producing his own children. Due to the damage done by radiation, he would likely develop secondary cancers and other lifetime illnesses that come with radiation treatments at such a young age. My husband and I would be willingly, without regrets, to care for him until we are physically incapable to do so. And we'd be able to have money put aside to hire paid care for him when it came to that. But how about love? Who would be there to give him the love he would be so dependent on, even when he was 30, 40, or 50 years old, the same as he was at three years old, when we were gone? Of course his sister adored and loved him, but is it fair to pass such a big burden onto her one day?

When the doctors told us that Max had relapsed, we decided that we would not subject him to any more chemotherapy. We knew very well that chemo drugs were only interim - they killed tumour cells, but not the stem cells that could prevent more cancer cells from growing. At the same time, chemo was also killing other normal cells. Max's body had been very much weakened by the eight rounds of heavy chemo treatments. He even suffered partial hearing loss from it. Chemo would only work for as long as your body could take it and we did not think that our son could take it anymore. There would be a point when his body could no longer take it then it would be the end of it - all the while suffering from all the toxicity before his body gave away.

As he was still too young to receive radiotherapy, Neil and I did lots of research, had consultations outside the hospital and gathered alternative treatments that many succeeded in curing, or keeping the cancer under control. We presented them to our oncologists who, expectedly, rejected us outright. From there on, we treated our son ourselves with natural supplements, cannabinoid oils and off-label drugs. They were all based on scientific researches, facts and experiments by real patients who in the end had more success than when they received conventional cancer treatments. Some were sent home to die, on hospice care, having nothing to lose and tried the treatments that would not harm the body in the process. Often these terminally ill patients outlived the time frame given by their doctors, and some even went into remissions. Yet, Neil and I often found ourselves asking if we were doing the right thing? We were certain that we did not want chemo for him nor radiation until we were desperate.

On the other hand, I never quite manage to shake off my doubt if Max would ever be able to walk on his own. At 15 or 16 months old, Max managed to walk a few steps unassisted. Then he gradually lost his balance towards his diagnosis. He was completely disabled after his brain surgeries; a complication we now know as posterior fossa syndrome. As the months went by, he regained part of his mobility, but not quite fully. He could crawl around but was not that interested in walking. He showed improvements with physiotherapy, yet he never quite got past balancing on his own. In our village, several babies were born when he was having chemotherapy. There were now all walking and running around. Sometimes, on days when nothing seemed to go well and I saw how these babies were chasing each other while I was still carrying Max around, my doubt quietly turned to pain.

CHAPTER 15

PAIN

Pain differentiates itself from other negative emotions by existing in both physical and mental forms. Two people can feel the pain originating from the same source in different forms, and I experienced that often throughout Max's cancer journey.

Pain, indeed, is the hardest negative emotion to process and let go of, especially for parents when the subject of concern is your own blood. It is almost against one's natural instincts to ignore that pain when you see your child is hurting. Wasn't it the bond, the connection between us which raised the alarm in the first place before anyone else noticed that my son was ill? When Max was in the operation theatre, he was under general anaesthesia and would not feel any pain throughout the operation. Meanwhile, I felt the pain in my heart throughout the seven hours until I saw him safe and sound in front of my eyes.

The kind of pain was difficult to describe. It was an intense form of sensation from the combination of negative emotions, namely, fear and guilt; and my vivid imagination of the pain that my son's body was going through. These emotions fuelled my imagination, and it was so intense that my body could not tell what was going on in my head from reality anymore. Except I was not the one who was being cut open nor bleeding, yet my body reacted to it and felt what the Chinese saying describes as, "like a knife stabbing into my heart".

The side effects from chemotherapy caused much physical pain for Max. His way of expressing such sensations, as best as he could for his age, was to cry for his mother to seek comfort. At the same time, it created pain within me - the hurting sensation of having to witness my child suffer. I swore at times the pain became physical. I lost count on the occasions when I could actually feel the stabbing pain I felt during his surgeries again. I understood why parents said they wished they could swap places with their children. Max needed morphine 24/7 to kill the pain. The grimace and shivering he gave me whenever I tried to wash his raw bum, which was bleeding and filled with yellow pus, hurt me too. He was so weak when his blood counts dropped to non-existent, and I wished I could stop the nausea that came in waves at my son. My heart broke for him and it pained me to see him like that.

When we learnt that it was possible that he had relapsed merely four months out of his excruciating chemotherapy, the pain from knowing that we could lose him quickly, was unimaginable. I went on to ask other 'unlucky' parents what it was like towards the end for their child. Was it painful for them? What can I do to make the pain go away? Should we listen to the doctors and subject Max to whatever harsh treatment they proposed, that would make him weaker and weaker in the name of trying whatever there's available?

Many parents opted for quality of life. They chose to have their sick children at home, to be surrounded by people who loved them when they spent their last days. Some chose to fight on, which bought them more time while their children went through more treatments. The decisions were personal, none right or wrong, yet definitely painful.

The pain of not being able to feel his weight and body warmth on me, not being able to hold his tiny hands, not being able to breathe in his unique scent, even not being able to change his foul smelling nappies, was like a stab to my heart, again.

Then, there was the experience of others who triggered the pain within us. I was on the social media page where parents of children who relapsed from brain cancer asked for advice, experiences with certain clinical trials, protocol for relapses, or simply asked for prayers for their dying children. As I searched the page for the information I was after, I came across so many that inflicted so much pain in me. One parent was describing the pain she felt while witnessing her child suffering towards the end. She was seeking help on how to get relief at home when the tumour on her son's spine had grown to the point that he was struggling to breath. As I was reading it, I felt that I was the one who could not breathe, the pain was simply too much, to the point that I was drowning and struggling for breaths from this imaginative searing pain.

CHAPTER 16

TAKE ADVANTAGE OF THE NEGATIVE ENERGY

Blame is the reflex action we often find ourselves doing at circumstances when negative emotions are involved. I myself am certainly guilty of this, especially during Max's battle with cancer. I tried my best not to blame consciously but since my husband accused me many times for doing that, I believe I was doing it unconsciously.

Instead, take advantage of that energy and do something that you always wanted to do. When you feel the negative emotions inside you, you have much energy ready to strike. If we are not careful, we can easily let that energy consume us, and do things that we will regret, or just simply not helping with the situation. Therefore, when you feel the negative emotions and become restless, consume that energy, otherwise it will consume you.

Thanks to my understanding of such a concept, every time I go through a very rough or stressful time in life, I direct my energy elsewhere. because actions derived from negative emotions never bring around anything good. However, if we use such energy on something else, without much expectation, a positive outcome will almost always guarantee.

Negative energy, albeit being negative, is still a kind of energy. This extra energy, if we let it run wild, will soon consume us. We feel restless, agitated, even if we do not do something about it. Yet, actions driven by fear, anger, resentment, doubt, jealousy… never bring anything good. Fortunately, we can make use of this energy and manipulate it to fuel us to do something positive and turn this negative energy around. I learnt this very early on when I first wanted to form a family.

The first time I miscarried, I was devastated - I felt my whole world was crumbling down. For days, I saw failure whenever I looked into the mirror. I finally fell pregnant after trying for nearly two years. I was at the top of the world. However, only weeks later all happiness was robbed from me.

One day, wandering around like a walking dead, I saw a banner overhead advertising yoga teacher training by a yoga studio. My mind clicked. It felt like an inspiration. I called the number on the banner and signed myself up to an evening part-time yoga teacher training course. I would have achieved something, no longer being the failure I believed I was, and hopefully in the meantime I would physically benefit from all the yoga and meditation training.

Ever since then, I applied this tactic whenever I went through some stressful time in my life. Learning new things and challenges are great ways to distract ourselves. The wall of the study in our household is a testimony of how much stress I have had in the past several years; it is filled with framed qualifications and certificates!

During the second month of Max's cancer journey, COVID went into full force and everyone in Hong Kong was fighting for face masks and toilet paper! We were the ones who needed the face masks most so as to protect Max from a single sneeze from any of us - yet, we had no opportunities to spare time to line up outside shops at two in the morning to buy one box of face masks that would only last for a few days for us. In the end, I decided that only we could help ourselves. I unearthed a sewing machine out of the deep corner of a cupboard, a wanted Christmas gift that had turned unwanted because of my lack-of-talent in the needle work department. I went onto YouTube to learn how to wind the bobbin. I had so much energy in me, mostly negative, that I learnt to sew face masks - the first of hundreds to come. I became so good at it that I started to sew for friends and families overseas, where face masks were even more sparse. Then I even turned it into a little profitable business, combining my love of fabrics, thanks to my previous career in the fashion industry, and made fashionable masks that could go with any outfits of the day. Many people had picked up baking during the pandemic lock down - but I was glad that I picked up sewing instead.

I liked making good memories during bad times. I learnt this valuable lesson from my fertility journey. Infertility, followed by repeated miscarriages, could drag you down. Now, with two lovely children and looking back to those dark days, I don't feel sorrow anymore. Instead, I feel proud of myself for getting through that and having built something for myself that benefited me for the rest of my life. The best thing I had done during that time was to sign up to do a yoga teachers' training programme. Although it was originally intended to distract myself as well as to help recover from my miscarriage, the qualification opened a new horizon for me. Since then I have continued to obtain other qualifications extended from the newly acquired skill set.

So, naturally I did the same again when we embarked on Max's cancer journey. Of course, I did not immediately do that. The initial weeks were simply overwhelming. We were still in shock and figuring out which way to go. However, after everything was settled and treatment began for Max, despite being exhausted, I made myself a promise to create some good memories during such challenging times, for myself and my family.

The first thing I did for myself was to pick up the stand-up paddling board that Neil had gifted to me for our anniversary the year before. Soon after receiving it, we entered winter and then unfortunately, Max got diagnosed with brain cancer in December. So, I told myself that by the time the water would become warm again Max would have had at least two cycles of chemotherapy, so we would know what to expect.

Let's do it, I decided, and so I did. It turned out to be fun, and soothing when I was out in the sea. It gave us much joy as it was something to share with my family. My husband and I would take turns to take the board out while the other watched the kids. When we were done with it, my daughter and her friends in the village loved using it as a diving board. They climbed up, steadied themselves, bravely jumped into the sea, then swam back to it and did it all over again.

Seeking balance on the SUP board had taught me an important lesson in life - keep your eyes on where you wanted to go, not down at where you are - or you would fall.

When the temperature dropped again, I decided to find something fun for my daughter to do. She's been amazing with her little brother, spending long periods of time at the hospital, and then she wasn't allowed to visit due to COVID. She started to miss him terribly and got upset about mummy and daddy not spending enough time with her. I wanted to look for an activity that she'd love enough to distract her. I particularly looked around the area where the hospital was located, so that when we took Max to the hospital she could share the journey in the car together.

In the end, I found the perfect sport for her. There's an ice skating rink near the Children's Hospital. Jasmine loved dancing so I went onto YouTube and found some figure skating clips. I asked if she would like to learn how to skate and spin like those graceful girls in the videos. She was intrigued and excited. She enjoyed taking ice skating lessons near where her brother was. Even when the ice skating rink was temporarily closed when COVID worsened, we switched to skateboarding. Neil also picked up the sports and found that he was a natural. I chose rip-sticks as I was paranoid about the skateboard slipping beneath me. In a way, we found ourselves sharing the same experience that Max had to go through to learn walking again after his brain surgeries. We all had some new balance to look for.

Years ago when my husband and I were still dating, we took a vacation to Beirut. We learnt that it's one of the best places to party in the world, because of its history of violent domestic wars. People simply did not know whether there's a tomorrow, so they made the best of each day and partied as such. These days, we threw party after parties at home - it was the perfect distraction from all 'scanxiety' from MRI's and fear of the future, and brought so much laughter and love to our house.

BIG STEP 3

ACCEPTANCE

The first step toward change is awareness. The second step is acceptance.
- Nathaniel Branden

Chapter 17

Why Me?

Why me? I have asked such a question numerous times in my life. Why was I the one to grow up without the love and protection of parents? Why was I the one who had to work three to four jobs to support myself through college while my classmates and friends could hang out and do all sorts of fun things? Why was I the one being bullied? Why was I the one who had difficulty getting pregnant? Then when I did, why was I the one who had multiple miscarriages? Why was I the one who had to go through the heartbreak of losing my babies? Why me? Why?

After Max was born and I felt I was done with babies, I reviewed my journey to motherhood and wanted to keep it a memory of how such an experience changed me. I wrote a book called 'My Rollercoaster Ride to Motherhood' under the pen name Orchid Bloom. It was a fiction that was 70-80% based on real events. The essence of the story was how the challenge to conceive and consequently fail to carry to full term brought me to begin my journey of healing - healing the wound of my childhood.

Growing up I carried the burden of feeling abandoned, unloved and unworthy. I felt that I had to earn everything: every attention and compassion. I did not know that I was worthy of love just by being myself. That unworthiness had brought lots of unnecessary hardships and heartbreaks. I fell prey to relationships or flings with men who did not deserve my time and thoughts, at all. But I felt so unloved, that the moment I saw the chance to get something to fill that void, I fell right into it - every single time.

Luckily, a dear friend who used to be my boss shared with me how she got out of a decade of entangled relationship and found the love of her life, someone who truly deserved her. She visualised in detail her perfect partner, how she met him, and what being in love and sharing her life with him was like. She said she made a vivid movie in her mind, in as much detail as possible. Later, she met the love of her life during a tango milonga, something she was passionate about.

I bagged this wisdom and did the same. I managed to stay single for nearly two years before I met the man who would later become my husband. I was like a drug addict who first had to go through a hurricane of itches before rising from the hell of it. I restrained myself from paying attention to any guy approaching me, as long as he didn't fit the perfect love movie that looped in my mind.

At first, it was hard, because I never lacked men paying me attention. Thankfully, I held onto the anchor of some platonic male attention; I had a few very good male friends who had no sexual interest in me. They just loved me for who I was. With their connection, I threw myself into voluntary work and travelled, sometimes on my own, to explore the world.

Chapter 18

Do Not Judge the Moment

That was the very first healing work I did to help myself, to get out of the vicious cycle of falling for unavailable men, because I failed to love myself and became needy of love. Yet, I was far from being healed, not until I could start a family of my own. Having babies became my obsession. I was so eager to have my own children so that I could shower them with the unconditional love I never had myself. How wrong I was.

I went through a period of darkness and depression from my infertility and miscarriages. This darkness opened the can of ugly worms of my childhood. I sought help. And among these helpers, someone told me that in order to become a mother, I had to be a child first. Without knowing it at that time, I had been led to the starting line of the healing marathon to my childhood. Along the run, I was reunited with my biological mother after being separated for more than thirty years. I took the time to get to know her and for us to get along with each other. The worst moments turned out to be a bearer of the next best things. And not long afterwards, at the finishing line, my daughter was born.

Without this life changing experience, I would have never started the healing of my life. I thought I was in total control once I became an adult and had become financially independent. I did not realise I had been unconsciously impacted by and even imprisoned in my past. It was the first time I learnt to hear my own inner voice, to honour the fact that I had all the answers within me - the answer to the question, 'Why me?', as long as I quietened my mind and listened. From there on, I learnt to trust the process of life, trust that everything happened for a reason, at the right time and right place, for the greater good to all those involved.

Millions or billions of people were going to remember their Christmas in the COVID year when we celebrated it in lockdown, some even had to be separated from their loved ones. Yet, for us we could hardly suppress our joy for the 'togetherness' we would be able to celebrate this year.

COVID turned out to be a blessing in disguise when Max had to go through a long and harsh chemotherapy. Although it was quite stressful during this pandemic, especially when Max's immune system was compromised, everyone around us became more conscious with personal hygiene and wore face masks. It actually made me feel better because we were not only concerned about the coronavirus, but any tiny little bacteria or some cold virus could be deadly to Max. I did not have to feel bad for not being able to visit families across the globe or that my daughter would be lonely when most of her play dates would be away for summer. Basically, the whole world was 'sucking it up' and staying home with us.

Yes, it was not easy with rules tightened up at the hospital but we only had to be creative and did more 'play' with Max ourselves. Whenever he was home between chemo cycles, we made every day a party for him. We were very lucky to live in the countryside, to be close to nature. We were minutes away from a stunning beach and handsome mountains where we could lose ourselves on the hiking trails. There was no better place to be when the whole world was trying to run away from COVID. And the candy on the cake? For the first time since we started seeing each other, Neil did not have to travel. All business trips were cancelled, and employees were asked to work from home. It gave us the luxury to have him around instead of just the weekends as it had been prior to COVID. He was able to 'work from hospital', spend time with Max during his breaks, and be my rock when I needed his emotional support.

There were many reasons to moan, to complain and to resent when undesirable circumstances arise. Yet, there were always two sides to a coin, and we could choose to see whether a glass was half empty or half full. I grew up poor but ended up working for the most luxury brand in the world for a significant part of my youth. Looking back, I realised it was not only the trade I had learnt from the job; there were many life lessons I had picked up as I learnt more about the brand value. The products they made often had an understated luxurious side to it. It was almost like they were playing tricks with their owners. You could only discover little surprises the more time you spent with them. I had come to look at life the same way - I waited for it to reveal itself, bit by bit, when the right moment came along. And expectedly, life was full of surprises and adventures always awaiting ahead.

CHAPTER 19

CHANGE THE PLAN, NOT THE GOAL

A goal without a plan is just a wish.
- Antoine de Saint Exupery

When a mother first finds out she's pregnant, if the pregnancy was desired, she probably starts to picture the future of her children and hers with her child in it. I did the same. Unlike his sister, Jasmine, our first born, Max was an unexpected pregnancy. We were content and already very grateful with Jasmine after years of trying. We were not even thinking of any more babies when I realised we could conceive without making much effort. I felt much more relaxed when I carried Max but it still did not stop me from making plans and setting goals, the moment I saw the double lines on the testing stick. Neil and I even amended our Wills, which were first made when we were married but child free. We even detailed our 'wishes' about how we would like our children to be raised, hoping the guardian we appointed in the unfortunate event of our demise, would honour our will. Like most parents, we prepared for the worst that might happen to ourselves and took measures such that our children's future was protected to some extent, and our goal did not change simply because we ceased to exist. Our Will allowed us to change the plan.

However, not many would expect it the other way round. How many parents would foresee or expect their children would fall seriously ill? That there would be a possibility that our children would not outlive us? Almost none. Yet, the unusual happened.

All roads lead to Rome. Unfortunate events in our life may delay how we reach our goals, but that does not have to be a denial. We do not need to give up our dreams, our goals and even ourselves just because our children fall sick. The mother of the sick girl in the movie

'The Fault in Our Stars'*, which was inspired by real events, had struck a chord with me. The main character was a teenage girl with many medical needs who threw her frustrations at her mother who had given up her job to look after her, and scolded her mother for wasting time on her. She threw in a big question asking what would her Mother do, when one day she was gone? It turned out her mother had been using the time she had to wait for her daughter in class and therapies to study a course that could help her to find a job that would help patients like her as well as their parents. It was a moving, inspiring story and taught us that plans could always be changed but not necessarily our goals.

We should also try to set intangible goals. Many parents set goals like 'becoming the top in class', 'go to Ivy League school', 'becoming a doctor, a lawyer or an accountant', 'buy a house, a holiday house and own at least two cars', 'marry a rich man and have two children'... the list goes on and on, yet they are all materialist achievement, and often doomed to fail and disappoint. Instead, we can help our children to set goals that are more ideological. How about, 'trying your best and seek improvement at exams', 'attend a school that offers the perfect environment for your subject', 'get a job that can support yourself and give you satisfaction', 'live a fulfilled life and be able to contribute to society'... There is a possibility that even if Max survives his cancer and lives a long life, that he would still encounter lifetime challenges as a result from his brain injuries and cancer treatment but my goals for him have not changed. I still want him to live happily every day. He can still live a fulfilled life and contribute to society. In fact, he has already does - by being an inspiration to many. His bravery and resilience is inspiring.

And I have not given up my personal goal. I still want to be a spiritual teacher, a life coach and help others to heal. I am now doing it in a format of a book, and I can offer online sessions, when I do not have to care for Max or my family. I have been writing during commutes, waiting for Max to have his rehabilitation session and when both he and his sister have gone to sleep. I may not have the luxury to do it in a leisurely way but what I do have is my determination, creativity to think outside the box, and flexibility to change the plan but not the goal.

Chapter 20

Awareness and Acceptance

Awareness is like the sun. When it shines on things, they are transformed.
- Thich Nhat Hanh

As a yoga teacher, I often emphasise the importance of awareness. A yoga practice typically begins in a sacred position, where we can calm down and become AWARE of the imbalance within our body. With beginners, whenever I demonstrate lateral poses, I always ask them to feel the difference between the left side and right. It is essential to help them become aware how the practice brings more space and length on the side of the body where they have just done the stretching. It's similar to the sales girl from a skincare counter showing you the effect on the half of the face after using their products.

Similarly, when it comes to cancer, we first need to be aware of its impact on our emotional well-being. Every week, I hear from parents, grandparents, wives, husbands, children, friends, and individuals saying or posting on social media about how much they hate cancer, or saying 'fuck you, cancer'. Obviously, it is not hard to imagine where the sentiments come from. I, myself, was totally guilty of it. I found myself saying numerous times to myself or others that I hate cancer. And even after Max had gone through a chemo cycle uneventfully, the after scan had come back clear, my first reaction was, 'fuck you, cancer.'

My husband even commanded, like a general, when chemo drugs were flowing through our son's system, "Come on, go kill those bastards!"

I was not aware how our anger and hatred for our son's condition affected us. We were easily irritated and angered by the hospital staff. We believed they didn't know better as they spent little time with the patient, our son. They were cold and unsympathetic because their children did not have cancer. Only, I had not been aware how much I wanted to control the situation but ironically had let the situation manipulate my emotions.

Being aware of the problem took me one step closer to the solution. I realised the root cause of it was because I was still in denial. I still could not believe it happened to me, happened to my child. Why does it have to be us? Go pick someone else! my mind screamed.

There was a nurse in the oncology ward, who was heavily pregnant when Max began his chemotherapy. She was one of the most gentle nurses and I felt lighter whenever I saw her on duty. One day late at night, when she came to refresh a new bag of IV fluid for Max, I found myself asking questions about her pregnancy. I learnt that it was her third baby.

"Working here and seeing the sick children everyday has not done any birth control trick on you already?" I joked. It seemed an innocuous question but deep down I really wanted to know her answer. Max was a surprise and I questioned myself more than once if I knew he would come with serious illness whether I would still want him.

"I cannot control what's going to happen, nor guarantee my child will be perfectly healthy, but I can certainly hope for the best and try my best to offer him the best of me," was her candid reply.

I was awestruck by the simple yet deep reply she casually conveyed. I knew the answer to the same question. I simply could not imagine my life without Max in it. I knew that it was time to accept it, to accept him as he was, even packaged with an incurable disease.

It was time for me to be able to say the words, "Max is my son, and he has brain cancer."

By accepting Max's cancer journey as part of my life and part of his, I was taking MY power back. I could not turn things around and wish the tumour did not exist in the first place. Being aware of how his condition impacted us, I could choose either being a victim and blaming everything on it, or accept the situation and make the best out of it.

BIG STEP 4

SHIFT THE FOCUS

CHAPTER 21

TINY STEPS, BIG SOLUTION

A journey of a thousand miles begins with a single step.
- Laozi

At school, students are not rewarded with full marks by getting the right answer to a mathematical problem. You get marked by each step towards the solution. Of course, when you are the student, you find it tedious. After all, you do get the correct answer. However, that is not the essence of education - the credit or value of training students to understand the problem and gear them towards the directions and the little steps it takes to get to the answer, that way the student is ready to tackle another same-but-different problem.

We always hear people say they never really use anything they learnt at school, at work or in their real life. After all, what do pure mathematical equations have to do with making a living unless you aspire to become an engineer, or a scientist? Yet, the value lies in the process and the logic we learn at school. How we come to tackle the negative emotions arising in our everyday life are similar to those tedious mathematical questions that appear on our exam paper at school. Once we learn how to deal with it, take small steps towards the solution, we can conquer them all, and find happiness and peace - the holy grail of all emotions.

Among all the modern day teachers whose works I have read, or done their workshops so far, I've found I associate the easiest with female teachers. They are usually uber intuitive and spit out words of supernatural and intelligence. As someone who I believe is also intuitive, I always trust my gut, and who is rarely wrong, I am attracted easily to a female teacher and absorb their teachings like a sponge to water. However, I remind myself again and again not to jump to the solution without knowing the steps: because by knowing how to get to the answer, I can flip it to whatever negativities I am to experience in my everyday life. So, once I know how to tackle fear, I then have the logistics and steps to deal with other equally disturbing emotions, such as doubt, anxiety, worries, resentment, etc.

Therefore, I read and learnt from male teachers, too. Like my husband and I, he was the questioner while I was more intuitive. I used my instinct to navigate life, most of the time successfully, while he questioned everything and eliminated obstacles. I valued the questions my husband threw at me every now and then, even at times when I found that annoying, but I know, my gut told me that he'd asked the right questions. We form a good team. When I was moving too fast, he slowed me down by asking the right questions, urging me to pause and think more and deeper. This had a similar effect and benefit that I always found the little steps and breakdowns from the male teachers, what they lacked in intuition, they compensated for it with logic.

I find it most helpful from 'Think Like a Monk', by Jay Shetty, on the topic of dealing with fear. The first step is to accept it, like you accept the test or exam paper where the questions are printed. Then you look at the problem and find out where it's coming from, so that you then know what theory or principle, the tools, you could apply to take you to the next step. This is a very important process in our analogy when we want to resolve our negative emotions. This is the stepping stone for us to detach from it, and to become objective to such emotion. This is the moment when we can turn the negative emotion into something of value.

Back to our mathematical equation, we now know what we need to do to take the next step closer to our solution. Take fear as an example; once you accept it and know where it is coming from, you can detach from the emotion and take yourself out of the situation. See yourself as a bystander and look at the fear objectively, then turn the fear into something of value, which leads to a constructive solution. Constructive fear is very valuable and essential in our life, like the fear of head injuries propel us to wear protective gear while attempting adventurous sports. Like scientists would tell you, stress in small doses is good for our body, because it will not pull us down, just act as a little stimulant to make us stronger.

Once we know how to turn that negative emotion into something of value, it reinforces what we do want out of the situation and resolve it into something positive. As Abraham would say, *knowing what you don't want, would clarify what you DO want*. Therefore, never estimate those little steps; those are the steps that would help our feet get out of the deep shit, and land us on solid ground.

We mentioned detachment. This is what it's all about in Buddhism. Despite going to Catholic and then Christian schools, my family and my culture embrace Buddhism, and I personally find it easiest to attune to. In the book, 'Sapiens (A Brief History)', by Yuval Noah Harari, Sapiens managed to become the dominating species by its ability to create imaginative stories and ideas that would convince millions and billions to believe and work towards the same theology. To me, Catholics and Christians are more about the stories in the Bible to prove that God existed, while Buddhism is ideological, with ideas that I can relate and apply to my everyday life.

The Buddhists' school of thought is, 'when you see everything as temporary, you would appreciate it more.' It is simple to prove it. Barely a few months after COVID hit the world in full force, there were reports from all around the globe with pictures which could be called miracles on earth. Thousands of turtles of rare species appeared on a deserted beach to lay eggs; oceans turned into a magical colour as an unusual marine life floated onto the surface and reproduce; at the zoo, pandas who were thought to be infertile, fell pregnant for the first time in a decade, once they were finally able to be intimate without the constant flow of visitors to be their audience. Once again, all these things showed us we are not what our egos made us think, that we are the owner of the Earth - we are merely its guests.

CHAPTER 22

LET GO

One of the happiest moments in life is when you find the courage to let go of what you cannot change.
- Unknown

My 40-year-old body was a lot more toned than my 20-year-old or 30-year-old ones. I had always exercised and was careful with my diet. I had no idea why my body type always leaned to the chubby side. Whenever I saw my friends who I hadn't in a while, they asked if I had put on weight again. I kept quiet as I did not dare to tell them I was actually on another diet and I was going to yoga three times a week. Yet, somehow I knew I always had a water retention problem. It's almost like my body blew up just by breathing and drinking. I even took supplements that claimed could resolve the problem, when I bought into the advertisement showing a woman's before and after pictures.

I stayed pretty bloated until I began my healing journey. Then the problem just went away on its own, without making any effort in diet nor exercises. I didn't even notice at the beginning, until the same friends commented that I finally lost weight and looked much lighter, happier. Only this time they wondered why I managed to do that when I was past my mid-30s. Then it dawned on me when I read Louise Hay's sensational best-seller 'Heal Your Body'. Apparently, people who suffered from oedema or water- retention could find it difficult to let things go. Same for those who constipate - literally could not 'let shit go'.

Just like for our body, which we need to detox regularly to stay healthy, our mind is the same; we need to rid it of the negative, poisoning thoughts in order to stay sane. As years pass, our guts become partially blocked by old rubbish that needs to be eliminated. Imagine the rubbish, unhelpful thoughts we have harboured in our mind over the years. Instead of going through uncomfortable and often dramatic detoxing measures like we do physically, we don't have to go through the same hardship for our mind - all we need is the willingness to 'let go'. Even if we did not know how, we could just affirm with 'I am willing to let go'. You would be surprised how things line up to help us.

Truthfully, before we can focus on the good things in life, we do have to clear the negatives first. Just like housekeeping, if we want to bring new things into our home, we have to do a purge so that we can give room to those fresh, good stuff. Fortunately for us, we don't have to physically move anything, as everything is in our mind. All fears, anger, criticism, resentments, doubts, hurt have been created by what we thought about things, people. Even self-hatred has been created by what we think of ourselves.

The most difficult word in the dictionary is 'let go'.
- Marisa Peer

Having a daughter meant I could not escape from watching Disney's princesses' movies hundreds of times and listening to their soundtracks even more. I was surprised by how much wisdom there was in those fantasies. Jasmine sang her heart out in the super hit song among girls of her age in 'Frozen'. She stomped her foot, pretending it was ice beneath her, spread her arms and sang the words:
Let it go, let it go, can't hold it back anymore....
Let it go, let it go, turn away and slam the door

Then came the part that spoke volume to me:
It's funny how some distance makes everything seem small.
And the fears that once controlled me can't get to me at all.
It's time to see what I can do.
To test the limits and break through.
No right, no wrong, no rules for me.
I'm free...

It's amazing how much wisdom is packed into songs that are aimed at children. We should all be listening to children's songs as those catered to adults were full of heartbreaks and problems. Indeed, when we try to detach ourselves and step away from the 'problems', every issue no longer seems big, they seem trivial instead. And the fears were just fears, they were controlling us only when we allowed them to, but in reality they could not get to us. What we can do is limitless. There is no right, no wrong, as all wrongs are only perceived wrongs. We are free. We have the freedom to choose our thoughts.

CHAPTER 23

GRATITUDE

Max's journey would have never begun without Dr Fanny Lam, a specialist in children's development. I shivered at the thought every time I went through the possibility of not having a doctor agree to give Max a MRI scan, that the tumour in his head would keep growing and he would sleep more and more until one day he just slipped away. Then we'd just find out what happened, that tumour happened, when an autopsy was carried out to investigate the cause of his death. So, we were immensely grateful for her and even during the tense period of one brain surgery after another, we did not forget to write to her to thank her for what she did for Max and for our family.

We were also extremely grateful for her colleague Dr Liu, who followed-up with Max's initial scan and provided swift arrangements for Max to be operated at the Queen Mary Hospital. Neil ran into Dr Liu, when he went to a nutritionist's office who specialised in cancer patients' diets, weeks after his surgery when he could finally swallow semi-solid food. Dr Liu was quite emotional when he asked about Max. He took it to heart about the discovery. We also found him visiting Max at the Children's Hospital and took the initiative to enquire about Max's progress on his chemo treatment. A few months' post treatment and at the one-year anniversary of Max's unfortunate diagnosis, we wrote to his clinic to update both him and Dr Lam on Max's health and expressed our gratitude again to them. They did not just return with a note of acknowledgment, they told us how thrilled they were to hear from us. They said they were very honoured to have met our son, who in their eyes, was a hero.

Max's brain surgeon Dr Ho, was a saint in parents' eyes. I found out later among other parents how Dr Ho would go to extra lengths to give us parents the confidence and reassurance we very much needed, as he did to us. A parent also shared the difference of the surgery outcome when the same surgery was performed by him and other surgeons. His tall physique and good looks stole the hearts of the medical staff, too. I had seen how the lady security guards reacted whenever he graced the ward with his visits. They thought he could walk on water!

After we found out about Max's diagnosis, we decided not to broadcast the news but rather to tell when asked about the well-being of our children. It was the right decision and I was glad that we did. Naturally, those who soon found out our dire situation were friends who genuinely cared. All of them - all offered their prayers, in their own ways or religions, for Max getting through his surgeries and excruciating chemotherapy as well as for his full recovery. We had churches in England saying prayers on Max's behalf; priests in Hong Kong summoned their followers to pray for Max; friends who meditated for his recovery in France, Belgium, New Zealand, and Japan. Gifts and toys for Max kept arriving from all over the world. We were overwhelmed and could not be more grateful by all the love and kind thoughts. I believed that the power of collective prayers had played an important role in Max's well-being throughout his treatment.

COVID made hospitals tighten up their visiting rules and not long into Max's chemo treatment, no visitations were allowed. Not only friends and families were banned from seeing patients, play therapists from charities such as the Children Cancer Foundation* was forced to stop. It was tragic for the children who had to stay for a prolonged period of time at each admission. COVID robbed the comfort and emotional support that was there before the pandemic.

Because of such inhumane but unavoidable measures, we were particularly grateful for the rehabilitation team at the Children's Hospital. The rehabilitation departments of the Hong Kong Children's Hospital play an important role in supporting paediatric patients there to recover. Max suffered something called Posterior Fossa

Syndrome after his three brain surgeries; he was paralysed from neck downwards. His swallowing ability and speech was hugely affected, too. Thanks to the physiotherapists, occupational therapists, and speech therapists there, Max had made tremendous progress during his chemotherapy.

The physiotherapists were a tireless bunch who carried heavy equipment around to help patients with their exercises. Most patients were constantly on an IV which hindered much of their movements. But you would see them work in a team, one helping the child while another wheeled the IV along as if it was part of the patient's body. As time went by, they learnt about what Max liked and made an effort to bring toys that would entice him as well as motivate him to take another step.

The Speech Therapist in charge of Max's case was one kind lady. She was almost apologetic every time when she had a session with Max, because she had been trained to give the therapy in Chinese, so she felt that it was not as good or as effective when she translated into English, Max's first language. I most remembered how she offered to help when Max vomited during one of her sessions. Most people would just jump as far away as possible and only approach when I was done changing Max and cleaning up.

But Miss Yo-yo asked me, "Mama, what can I do to help?"

I nearly hugged her if my hands weren't full of puke.

Then we had Miss Helen, the Occupational Therapist. She and her team had gone way and beyond to make our stay much easier and comfortable. The furniture in the wards were not meant to be for young toddlers, let alone those with disabilities. We were only given an iron crib that was on loan from another hospital. As a result, we had to haul lots of furniture with us each time we checked in. Then, because we were only given a very short notice before we were discharged, we often struggled to carry everything back, especially since we lived up on a hill in the countryside. We asked many times for basic furniture such as a high chair for Max to sit in safely. The response was always, "No, what you see is what you get," or words to that effect. Finally, it was Miss Helen who arranged all the needed supporting furniture and safety cushions for us as part of Max's rehabilitation programme. Our stay would have been much different and challenging without her help.

The final three cycles of Max's chemo treatment required stem cell transplants as the rescue from high dose chemo which was expected to wipe out his bone marrow. We were terrified during that period because of the grim picture that had been painted to us prior to the process. Up to 10% of the patients who were admitted to that ward did not make it, so given Max's conditions and our not so pleasant experience at the Oncology Ward, I requested to meet the Ward Manager beforehand. I explained the challenges we faced in the other ward and explained why we needed certain support. I half expected my requests would be dismissed like they did at the Oncology Ward. However, as it turned out, every point I raised had already been taken into consideration. All the nurses and doctors were kind and empathetic. They could not be more helpful and our stay was smooth and uneventful. I particularly remembered one bad night when I snapped at the doctor who was unlucky enough to come check on Max. Two days later I went to find her to apologise for the other night. She shrugged and told me not to worry about it. She said it must be very hard to have to go through what we were going through. I was grateful for her understanding as well as her compassion for us parents.

It seemed that there was only one clinical psychologist at the Children's Hospital who had to shoulder all requests concerning patients' and their caretakers' emotional well-being. Yet, each time when Miss Ada paid Max a visit to have a play session with him, she gave it her all and I had never seen a more enthusiastic therapist. Max's eyes lighted up whenever Miss Ada entered his room. She also answered my wish to do music therapy with Max when he became more irritated as a result from his brain surgeries. In other countries such as the United States, there was a ritual or a ceremony for every warrior who braved through cancer treatment. I asked the doctors and nurses whether they had rituals like 'Ring the Bell' to celebrate when the treatment came to an end. They said, "no," and declined my suggestion. In the end, it was Miss Ada who came on the last day of Max's cancer treatment and presented him with a much deserved Certificate of Bravery.

As Max left the care of the hospital and the required blood check became less frequent, there were community nurses who would come to our house to care for the port line on his chest. The line was used during his chemotherapy for easier administration of chemo drugs, IV medicine, and as well as blood draw. We were so grateful for such services as it saved a three hours commute for us just to have Max's port line flushed with saline solution. The community nurses were kind and friendly. They did not mind the never ending questions Max's sister had about nurses and often they brought treats for both Max and Jasmine, just to bring a smile on those little faces!

We had never been more grateful to the Hong Kong Government who sponsored most of the medical treatments Max had received so far. Neil joked that we finally got our value back after paying taxes for that many years. Not only were our surgeries, chemo treatments, hospital stays, and doctor fees heavily subsidised, the Social Welfare Department also sponsored the rehabilitation programme for Max after his chemotherapy. The social worker in charge of Max's case at the hospital had helped us with a placement at a brand new rehabilitation school which was run by a well-established non-profit organisation in Hong Kong. The training school was only a ten minutes' drive away from our home which allowed Max to preserve his energy for the rehabilitation activities in class. The therapists were kind and experienced. Despite having sessions back to back, I did not see their enthusiasm reduced. They were Max-oriented and very encouraging towards us parents. We could not be more grateful for having such support for Max until he was ready to join the mainstream education.

Chapter 24

Appreciation

Nature is what I came to appreciate most during my son's cancer journey: the soothing green of the bushes, the vibrant colours of the blooming flowers, the grounding sensation of the sand when I stepped onto the beach, the gold sparkles radiating from the sea - all were strong contrasts to the cold and clinical set-up at the hospital.

One day when I was pregnant with my daughter, I picked up a newspaper at the library; I couldn't remember the last time I'd read a physical newspaper. Anyway, I flipped through it and came across an advertisement of a super luxury development on an island. That day, I decided to go home and tell my husband that I'd like to raise our child there - not in that deluxe mansion, as we could not afford it, but on that island, to be surrounded by nature and beauty. Two weeks later after making a cold call to a couple of property agents, we went to the island to look at houses in different villages and we finally found the house we live in now.

Like everything had been aligned, we made an offer to the owners with a significant reduction, which was rejected. But somehow months later they came back to us to accept our offer as we were the ones who would agree with their terms of transactions. Our village beach had even been featured on CNN as one of the hidden gems in Hong Kong. As one of its residences, we were so proud of such an endorsement while at the same time we hoped this secret never went out. I felt so lucky we made the decision to move far away from the hustle bustle of the city.

Beautiful nature is now at our doorstep. There was no better place for my daughter to be during COVID lockdown. I ground myself whenever possible on our precious beach, to connect with Mother Nature and my inner being. I also take it everywhere with me. Whenever I need to stay calm, I close my eyes and visualise the sparkling sea, which has become my anchor of peace.

And the air! I've never appreciated breathing fresh air in, so much in my entire life. At the hospital, we had to wear face masks and a protective gown at all times, to protect Max from us breathing beings. Sleeping with a face mask on when I spent the many nights with Max was the most uncomfortable. Wearing a mask while lying down was like having someone's hand on your nose and mouth - it felt so suffocating. I found it difficult to breathe, let alone sleeping. I had a new perspective and mostly respect for everyone who worked in the clinics, care centres and hospitals, to gear up in those plastic or paper accessories all day long on a daily basis.

The Hong Kong Children's Hospital began its operation in June, 2019. We felt very lucky, out of very unlucky circumstances, that Max was diagnosed in December the same year that we got to be transferred to the newly established medical facility, just for children patients, whose illnesses require multidisciplinary attention and care. Until then, the paediatric department of respective public hospitals took care of young patients, whereas standard and resources might vary. At the Hong Kong Children's Hospital, all care was converged and standardised, as its motto said, putting children first.

Its location was where the notorious Kai Tak Airport used to be, which was relocated to the reclaimed part in the north of Lantau island in 1997. Kai Tak Airport used to be a landing skill test for pilots since the runway was inches away from residential buildings. Passengers used to have a ritual to give their captain a round of applause when the plane touched the ground with everyone aboard safe and sound.

You could nearly feel the excitement at that time being inside the Children's Hospital. The hospital was indeed standing along a stretch of flat land, adjacent to the water, which was now the bay or a terminal of luxury cruises coming from near and afar.

I cannot think of a better infrastructure to build on such a legendary airport than a hospital that catered to the great need of sick children, and a research centre for the purpose of looking for the cure. Everyone from everywhere usually has lots of complaints against their government but during this time we were more than grateful for the decision ours had made to continue the legend of the old Kai Tak Airport.

The design and decoration at the Hong Kong Children's Hospital is colourful and delightful. Not only is it looking over the renowned Victoria Harbour, the interior warms your heart as soon as you walk in. Despite having been there many times, I discovered a little something new every now and then. The first things that welcome visitors are the delightful colours. The 'children' of the Hong Kong Children's Hospital was written in different colours; yet the colours are bright and joyful but not overwhelming nor intimidating. The interior is animal themed.

Max learnt his first animals inside the six elevators that go up to the wards. Panda, koala, monkey, dolphins, octopus and the parrot inside the wards had become familiar. Jungle and the sea themes spread across various wards and special departments, and as many kids who frequent the Children's Hospital need scans at the Radiology Department, they are in for the surprise to explore even Space!

I was particularly impressed by the details that the designer managed to cover like the koala, panda and monkey that enabled functional items such as fire alarms to blend into the jungle that spread along the walls all over the hospital. The marvellous use of friendly animals has not only been used to mask boring fixtures but are also applied to scary machines like the x-ray that is often used to investigate further medical conditions. Instead of a cold, clinical x-ray machine, you would see a giraffe roaming around and have the children intrigued by its long neck which was actually the arm that brought the spotlight and camera around to do its work. And how thoughtful it is to apply round and smooth edges all over, which takes a few more visits and bored moments to notice. All the counters, walls whatever possible, are finished with round edges and minus the sharpness that you usually find at any other hospital.

I was never someone who liked taking photos, but these days I have over 10,000 photos and videos, combined on my phone and iCloud. With the technology nowadays, our phone lens is as good as, sometimes even better, than the conventional camera. Not to mention a special app that allows us to do further editing. We used to tease others who were too busy to take pictures or videos to enjoy the moments, but having those photos and videos are precious to us parents and even grandparents, friends, and families, who care and want to see each other. With miles between us, I am able to update grandmas and grandpas with videos and photos of their beloved grandchildren. This is just indisputable during hard times like COVID when families are forced apart for a prolonged period of time. Thanks to this amazing technology, we are connected and continue to feel the love for each other as long as Wifi is available. I am even writing this book on my phone when I don't have my computer with me. I am able to write a bit here and there, then I can email the words to myself, or simply save it into the cloud.

I choose to believe that because we spent most of our time in the ward with nurses that's where most of the conflicts were. I chose to believe everyone in the hospital tried their best to help patients and their parents. I particularly appreciate the supporting teams in different departments.

The medical assistants in the ward were mostly young grandmas. They were very gentle with Max and most emphatic with us, mummy and daddy. Max didn't like to have his blood pressure taken and the grannies often had their tricks to distract him - after all, a distressed patient meant high blood pressure. After they took the vital readings, we were always the first ones to learn about them even though they were only obliged to report to the nurse. These little reassuring gestures mattered, because kindness mattered.

Music had played an important role during Max's cancer journey. I came to really appreciate the singers' voices, with so much emotion in them that the audience could easily resonate. As I rotated with Neil between home and hospital so we could spend time with both of our children, I chose to spend the nights with Max at the hospital as it's when he usually looked for mama when he woke up. I found myself always listening to, 'I Gotta Feeling', by Black Eyed Peas. It was a great song and tune to boost my mood and tell my mind to visualise a great night ahead. Anything could happen during the nights; from disturbances of nurses coming in to check on Max, taking vital signs and giving injections, to an unexpected fever that would cause a series of motions as blood had to be drawn to check for infections. There were also times when something or someone triggered the fire alarm at the hospital - then it would be hours before peace would fall upon the wards once more. As I hummed along to the lyrics and swayed my body to the tunes, my body felt energised and my mind was made to believe, 'that tonight's gonna be a good night'. It set me in the right mood when Max saw me. My enthusiasm was contagious. Max was excited to see me every time. It was a perfect way to ease off the boredom from the confinement in the ward and light up the mood to start the evening.

When morning came, after a series of commotions, breakfast, and Max had settled down to play in his high chair, I handed Max over to the 'day team'. Then I would put my Air Pods into my ears and begin to wind down. I applauded the genius of the music engineers as I listened to audio clips of three-dimensional sounds. It expanded the space inside my head. It was a perfect filter for all the tension from being the only caretaker for a sick child. It helped me relax and I often managed to fall into a deep sleep, even just for half an hour; it refreshed me before I arrived home to give my all to my other child waiting at home.

CHAPTER 25

HOPE

I have never appreciated the existence of social media until Max's diagnosis. I have always thought media such as Facebook shared too much of our personal information, or it's a time and energy consuming pastime to post envy-worthy pictures. However, when you were lucky enough to know very few people who had experienced cancer themselves, let alone having cancer kids, you would be desperately wanting to connect with people who do, who could tell you what they know about the illness; in other words, who spoke the cancer language.

Even with brain cancer there were a number of types. No one I knew had any clue what I was talking about when I mentioned the word 'Medulloblastoma'. Bear in mind, that paediatric cancer was so rare that eight doctors had seen Max but failed to connect the dots that something was very wrong with his brain.

At first, I associated such groups as venues where parents met with parents who could relate to them, who understood what they were going through. When Max was still going through surgeries, however, I stopped visiting that page because for a while, I only saw post after post about kids losing their battles to cancer and who gained their wings to heaven. It was depressing and demotivating when we'd just started our fight. However, when all hell broke loose after the first cycle of chemo, and Max was suffering horrible side effects, I felt like I had no one to turn to. Doctors cared little about discomfort and pain but I knew that parents of kids going through the same treatment would do.

This time round, I logged on with the intention to look for supplements and aids that could help us better prepare for the following rounds, to minimise the side effects that Max would have to endure. I could not believe my eyes. My mind was blown away. Not only could I find answers to all the questions I had regarding Max's illness, I was amazed and impressed by all the scientific research and medical articles other parents shared on the group page. You would have believed them if they claimed they were medical professionals. The expansive knowledge they possessed and the depth of details they were capable of explaining at times convinced me that they knew more about this particular cancer better than our oncologists. Soon I understood the difference between us parents and the doctors - while they were treating the symptoms, we were trying to look for a cure. For the first time in weeks, I felt hopeful. You could not help but feel your heart soar when you read about years of survival when the doctors told the parents their children had only months to live. I particularly appreciated the tips I could get on the day-to-day care of children who had Posterior Fossa Syndrome, that affected walking, talking, and emotional issues. These parents, with their generosity in sharing their knowledge and compassion, had given me the hope and strength to carry on.

I then went on to discover more pages and groups that provided the public with information that even doctors would not have the time and will to go through. Facebook organised discussions in a way that group members could easily comment, share links to articles on the Internet, and you could easily search for topics by looking up on threads with the relevant keywords. Even sitting in the comfort of home, or the discomfort of the hospital, I could feel the healing power, energy, and synergy through having the sharing of information at my fingertips. Strangers all over the globe were united together by a common tragedy who shared a single hope, through the engine of what we call social media today.

Parents of other child patients that I met at hospital, through friends, on social media, kept putting me in awe. Their strength and love for their children never ceased to inspire and motivate me. Indeed, in some of our darkest moments they were the ones who lifted me up.

The very few parents I met after Max's diagnosis were the 'permanent residents' at the paediatric ICU. The ward had a strict rule of visitation due to the intensive care required of the patients there. Parents were only allowed to visit between 12pm and 8pm. Although we were gutted to have to leave Max alone overnights, we were comforted by the fact that there were nurses who could attend to him 24/7, and we got to go home to put our daughter to bed, have a rest, and spend time with her in the morning before leaving for the hospital again.

Every day, we arrived at the waiting hall outside ICU at 10 minutes before noon, sharp, waiting to get the clearance from the security lady who would call the number of Max's bed, No. 6, and let us through to see our son. After a few days on, we began to recognise familiar faces. These faces gave us a nod whenever they saw us, encouraging smiles whenever they saw motions of Max being pushed to another floor for another department to do this scan or something bigger, or for another brain surgery. Some parents came for their new-borns who were born prematurely, as the neonatal ICU was within the paediatric intensive care. The mothers still looked like they were about to give birth, and were always carrying an ice box which I assumed was filled with milk they pumped at home. Among the parents who we started to greet each day at 5 minutes to noon, three pairs of them were parents of Max's neighbours.

The one that left me most awestruck was 'Mother Teresa'. Teresa was Joseph's mum. Joseph was a thirteen months old who suffered some intestinal problems. He was Max's immediate neighbour. Together with the three-year-old girl next to him, they had been taking up residence at the ICU since birth. Despite the cold clinical set-up, Teresa managed to create a little nursery haven for Joseph. Every afternoon, while my husband and I tried to hold Max's hands, talk to him to get some responses from him, Teresa sang and danced to get all those angelic giggles from Joseph. It felt more like in a playgroup than in an intensive care unit.

Without knowing it, Teresa's strength and enthusiasm grew on me. She seemed so happy and at ease. One day we were delayed to be allowed in as they were changing Max's dressing on his head. The nurses were also working on Joseph. As the only parents singled out, I started a conversation with Teresa, hoping I could get some tips out of her. I knew that Joseph had been there since birth, so by the guess of his age, she'd been doing that for over a year. I did not sense any resentment in her. She told me the many close calls they experienced in the past year, but they were content her son was doing well and gaining strength gradually. Her biggest regret was not having enough time for her older son. However, from my observation, her family had already adapted their new life around Joseph. They adjusted their daily routine by a few hours; they went to bed late to stretch their evening so that she and her husband could spend time with their elder child. Teresa also made her social calls at the hospital. I often saw her having lunch with her friends at different cafes and restaurants within the hospital complex. She never complained and turned Joseph's area into a little play corner. Her wish was to bring her son home by the following Christmas.

Lying next to Joseph was a three-year-old girl who had a problem with her lungs. To my absolute horror, I learnt that she'd been living in the PICU ever since she was born. Every other day she had to breathe in steam to moisturise her lungs. Her respiratory system was so messed up that her doctor said he'd have a hard time when one day he would need to hand her over to another paediatrician. I heard him joke one day that he was going to walk her down the aisle in that ward! I could not imagine what life was like for her parents. Yet, her mother was there every day by noon on the dot when we could be allowed in to visit.

The inner strength demonstrated by these mothers had given me so much hope without them realising it. Their children were in a more dire condition than mine, but they never thought of giving up on their children, not holding any grudges towards the situation. If they could do it with so much peace and grace for that long, I was not going to lose hope on myself for doing at least half as well.

Chapter 26

Love Thyself

There's nothing you can do that can't be done.
Nothing you can make that can't be made.
No one you can save that can't be saved.
There's nothing you can know that it isn't known.
Nothing you can see that isn't shown.
There's nowhere you can be that isn't where you are meant to be.
All you need is love.
Love is all you need.
- The Beatles

We all know that everyone needs love. Our focus of the source of love is often on romantic relationships, bonds with our families, as well as friendships we have built throughout our life. Indeed, the commercial world profits from our neediness of love. Advertisement demand soared whenever there was a television series that showed a family drama that captured the audience's hearts and earned their tears. The beauty industries created an illusion of finding love when certain products were used to improve physical appearances. In other words, marketing that banks on emotions worked because the fundamental need within us is LOVE. And we would never be able to fill that void if we are dependent on others for love.

We look into the mirror every day to groom ourselves, yet we miss the person with whom the relationship is the most important one in our life - our own very self. We are the only person that will stay with us from the beginning till the end. Louise Hay once said, there is one single solution to all trivial problems we encounter every day, as well as big problems like wars; that solution is self-love.

The reason is very simple - when we love ourselves, we naturally expect good things to happen to us. We do not have to stress, compete, or fight for what we want. The self- worthiness that we have within us makes us feel good. These good feelings charging within us constantly draws and attracts good experiences into our life. This idea is as simple as it is complicated to apply, because right from childhood we are taught to love families, friends and even our enemies. We simply do not know it is essential to love ourselves when no one teaches us to. People also have developed some habits throughout their lives doing just the opposite, without realising it.

To love ourselves, the first step is to STOP blaming, criticising and punishing ourselves.

In my line of work, I get to work with many mothers, both first time mums as well as second or even third time parents. I have the privilege to help mothers who have recently given birth to recover their physical well-being. As an extension of my prenatal and postnatal yoga teaching training, I went on to learn the art of postnatal wellness therapy, belly binding. Most misunderstand that belly binding is solely squeezing and binding the mother's belly back to its pre-pregnancy size. In fact, it is a therapy that helps a mother to recover from childbirth, to realign the body by shifting the internal organs to their rightful positions. I find that mothers feel very vulnerable during the early days of motherhood, especially for those who had experienced childhood trauma - they often had their whole early life playing in their mind while watching their very own child. I have seen mothers who were looking forward to having their babies become an angry mum who struggled to give her love to her new-born. They did not experience postpartum depression; they were simply angry. Seeing their child brought back all those childhood dramas and she began to compare herself with her parents as caretakers. It's the best time for them to process and to heal, if not, the hurt would be buried further and impact their relationship with their own children.

Carrying a baby for nine months then going through an intense labour to bring a child into the world is one of the most physical testing activities for mankind - yet, after the birth, almost all the focus of care is on the baby. Very few pay attention to the needs of the mother. On the contrary, the demand for the mother to be on her feet, to breastfeed, and to look after the new-born is generally expected right away. From there on, a mother is expected to give and give.

Some mothers decide to do the belly binding because they are finally 'done' with having babies after the second or third one. I particularly see the effect of the never ending demand on these mothers. They are often overly tired, struggle to get through their busy days, a bit lost in their own identity, and most importantly, they have little self-love for themselves. I always ask the mother the question why they come to have the belly binding. Nearly 90% of them have the same answer - they want to restore their figure. They don't really care about the benefit of the detox, realignment of internal organs, nor restoring their energy through the process. So, I found it's a perfect opening for me to share with them the importance of self-love. I tell them that if they want to lose weight, restore their figure, and experience the vitality they have lost long ago - the answer is very simple - to practice self-love.

It is not an easy concept to permeate into these mums' heads who have been spending every day, every moment of their lives, serving their families but not themselves. So, I have learnt to make an analogy to connect how loving themselves helps them love their children and families. I give them the example of the giant pivoting bucket in a water park. Visitors, both young and old, gather under the bucket, anticipating with excitement, for the bucket to fill up. Once the bucket is full, by the laws of physics, it will tilt and splash over EVERYONE. I tell the mothers to imagine themselves as the big bucket as many are waiting to get her love. Fill your bucket first - then it becomes effortless to pour your love onto those who need it. Happy Mum Equals Happy Family.

"Don't forget to make yourself happy," I say to them all the time. "My mama friends tease me as the Queen of Indulgences. A happy person is very attractive, so everyone wants to spend time with you. They are willing to make things work around your busy family life.

Your marriage, friendship, partnership, all relationships that you care for, fall naturally into place, just by being happy. It is that simple."

The second step to learning to love ourselves is to learn how to let go and relax. Learn to stop all self-blaming, self-criticising, and self-punishments - let them go. DO NOT question yourself and go through the cycle similarly. Relax. When you relax, it becomes easier to let go of all negative emotions. We will only have room to allow positive emotions to come in if we clear space for them.

It's similar to gardening, in order to allow our seeds to sprout, we need to keep clearing the weeds. By relaxing ourselves, we also allow ideas and inspirations to flow in. Actions will be inspired. Actions through inspiration always bring positive results. When you are inspired, you can be the busiest person on Earth without feeling the fatigue. Inspirations are that powerful - they fuel us with energy. And we can tap in this energy by simply relaxing ourselves. Hence, doing things to help ourselves relax is self-love. Having a long, hot bath, going for a massage, walking in nature... loving ourselves is simple, and enjoyable.

Then the mothers protest about not having time to do things for themselves. Yet, the treatment of belly binding through taking time out on a daily basis to have such therapy shows them that it is POSSIBLE to take time out to have some self-caring.

A lot of mothers enter motherhood without realising the importance of self-love. They put their children first, to the point that they forget about caring for themselves. Over time, they become confused about their identity, they are too busy mothering and struggling to be a wife, a daughter, a colleague, a friend, etc. They begin to question their life purpose, as if without their children, they are nothing.

Once we are relaxed, the next step is to learn to approve and praise ourselves. Self-approval and constant praising help us not to return to the vicious cycles of self-demeaning and punishing. It boosts our self-esteem. Sometimes people get confused between self- esteem and ego. They are two very different things. Self-esteem finds its way to love itself, while ego wants everyone to love it. Which is easier? Of course it's the former as it is impossible and exhausting to have everyone love us.

The next step and the most effective, powerful way to love ourselves is to feel self-worthiness - to believe that we deserve. When you believe you deserve good things, naturally you would not settle for anything that is less than that. I even picked up a habit to remind my daughter to love herself. Jasmine likes counting the people she loves in her life, especially during bath time.

"I love mummy, daddy, and my baby brother Max," she always says.

"Don't forget to love yourself," I always reply back to her, every single time.

After a while, she began to say, "I love mummy, daddy, my baby brother Max, and myself!"

She does not quite understand what it really means to love herself but it does not matter. I want that statement to permeate her subconscious mind from a young age.

When we were babies and growing up, we depended on love from our parents, caretakers, and families. Without their love, we could not possibly thrive or even survive. However, if we do not learn to love ourselves, once we are adults, or believe that we are worthy of good experiences, we become needy for love and be forever looking for people and material things to fill that void. Alcoholics, shopaholics, smokers, eating disorders, and the tendency to keep falling for partners that are unworthy of our love are all signs of lacking self-love. I realised that it is one of the most precious pieces of wisdom I can share with my daughter, such that she would never settle with second bests, do things to please other people but herself, and save her from heartbreaks with unworthy relationships. I believe, when she loves herself enough, she will live a happy, healthy, and fulfilling life. Indeed, I think it is one of the most important lessons we can teach our children, girls in particular.

Loving myself is an indispensable anchor when things seem to get complicated and a spider-web of emotions build up within me. I can imagine why such a simplest concept could be the most complicated to absorb. Practising what I preach, I remembered to care and love myself despite the enormous demand of Max's diagnosis on my time and energy. With him being at the hospital and his sister at home, we were in survival mode. Both Neil and I exercise regularly; we both agreed that it was essential to stay healthy and fit for our children at such a critical time. It was time that we had to be creative and think outside the box.

We found, despite having ten elevators in the hospital building, the overwhelming number of patients, visitors, and staff made the life waiting time long and tedious. Two days in, we decided that we would use the stairs to commute between wards and different departments for scans and tests. The paediatric intensive care unit was on the tenth floor - quite doable for a healthy adult to handle. With visiting hour breaks, moving to different buildings for various tests and check-ups, I reckon we each climbed over one hundred floors every day during my son's stay when he was recovering from his brain surgeries. We were a bit out of breath at the beginning but towards the end of our son's stay, we could easily chat our way up without a change of colour on our faces.

When Max was moved to the Children's Hospital for his chemotherapy treatment, the staircase was not open to the public. I became the 'Yoga Mama' who carried her yoga mat along with my son's belongings every time we checked into the hospital. Thanks to COVID, only one caretaker was allowed to look after our son. Despite this, I still managed to steal time here and there to get onto my yoga mat. I like starting my day with five to ten minutes of yoga to boost my energy level as well as unlocking the muscles that tense during sleep. After doing the morning routine, I would put Max into his high chair and bring out toys for him to play with. When the nurses and assistants came around in the morning to fuss around him, drawing his blood for tests, taking his temperature, blood pressure level and so forth, I could sneak in my morning yoga sequence. As soon as Max went to sleep in the evening, I set up my 'yoga studio' in the bathroom, since that was the only place I could take my face mask off and remove the protective gown. No one would believe me if I told them I spent a year doing yoga in a bathroom of a public hospital. Yet everything is possible, we just need to be creative and think outside the box, and act out of love for ourselves. And there is no better time to love ourselves than in this moment, in this place. Love yourself here and now. If we wait until we have achieved certain goals before we can love ourselves, we will never get there. If we can love ourselves just as we are, then when things improve, we will find it even easier to love ourselves more, and that would only lead to one outcome - a joyous and loving life awaiting us.

BIG STEP 5

FORGIVENESS

CHAPTER 27

HEAL YOUR BODY

All illnesses are caused by being Unforgiving.
- A Course in Miracles

I first came across the idea of a 'metaphysical body' when I attended a meditation workshop by Melinda Sutanto from the Golden Space* with a friend who was leaving Hong Kong. She was looking for someone to go with her to an activity that most would regard as 'hippy'. I did not really care what it was, I just wanted to spend more quality time with her before her departure. Besides, I had been meditating for years, so I was sure there would be something new for me to learn. I went with an entirely open mind, and my mind was blown away.

Melinda made an introduction to the class 'Heal Your Own Health' with a story of her own; how she had a recurring medical condition that none of the conventional medical treatments could resolve - it just kept coming back to the same point until someone suggested to her to try meditation. She gave it a go without expecting a miracle. After all, what could 'just sitting there and focusing on breathing' achieve when doctors and surgeons with various medical degrees failed to help?

For the first few times, she did not feel any difference physically but she felt much lighter emotionally. Through the guided meditation by her mentor, she resolved some emotional wounds that had been buried deep within her years ago, coincidentally around the time when the medical condition arose. Each meditation led to more healing until one day, she could notice the medical condition was going away, and this time round, unlike before that it kept returning surgery after surgery, it never came back.

Melinda went on to explain how our body, the internal organs, responded to every emotion we feel, almost like a lock to every key. As she walked us through ailments of each body part and the corresponding emotions, the studio was awe-struck. It was so accurately described. Each of us seemed to have some physical conditions and when Melinda stated the possible causes, she could not be more spot on. If she could assess your emotional state, it was quite possible that she could tell you about your health without having to do a blood test nor X-ray.

My friend who invited me to join her had recently recovered from acute asthma. She was one of the healthiest persons I knew and she went hiking every morning with her dog. She never had any respiratory problems, so how on earth could she suffer from asthma at the age of 40? It turned out she had experienced a dramatic heartbreak shortly prior to the asthma attack. According to Melinda, our chest and lungs took the toll when we felt hurt in our hearts. A year later, I met a lady who suffered from the early stage of lung cancer. I was not surprised, she's been deeply hurt by her ex-husband and more lately, her ex-boyfriend.

As I listened to Melinda decoding each of my fellow classmate's physical conditions, I suddenly had this 'ah-ha' moment, and it answered a puzzle I had been trying to solve ever since I had received the great news from my doctor that my Hepatitis was gone. My sister and I were both born with Hepatitis B, a chronic liver inflammatory illness that was quite common among Asians in our generation. Most of us got it at birth from mothers who did not even know they had the condition themselves, like in our case. Nowadays, you can screen the virus from a simple blood test and give your new-borns a few jabs at birth and several months afterwards, none of it would affect your next generation.

One of the symptoms of Hep B is fatigue. A person with Hep B needs lots of rest. When I was in university, I was doing full credits while having three, sometimes four, part-time jobs to support myself, and despite being at a young age, I was always tired to the bones. This flared up the inflammation of my liver to an alarming level. Yet, without knowing I had such a condition, as our father never told us since he did not know either, I was shocked to find out I had this serious chronic illness when the hospital conducted a routine blood test before they pulled all my wisdom teeth out. I had been on medication ever since and was told that I had to take that little blue pill until the day I died in order to keep the inflammation under control.

Fast forward to fifteen years later, once when I had my routine blood test and check up with the doctor at hospital, I was sent to do a number of tests like the ultrasound to confirm the condition of my liver. I got quite nervous as I wondered if my Hep. B had become worse. Only when the doctor told me they were going to try to take me off the medication, I was delighted by the news, but at the same time puzzled how it happened. According to the doctor, the antigens were gone, which I had been told was not possible as it was there when I was born, and since I did not get any vaccinations at birth, the condition stayed in my DNA. The doctor could not explain why but at the same time did not call for celebration. I was still asked to have regular check-ups in case there would be a 'flare-up' after I stopped the medication. I had been wondering what had caused the miracle to happen as I wanted to remain Hep. B free and bid a permanent farewell to the little blue pill. I finally had the answer to this mystery at Melinda's workshop.

Growing up I had always been angry with my parents. I blamed them for all the hardships I had to go through because they were not there to protect me and to love me. The anger also reached a new level when I was at university because I had to financially support myself. I was the only one in my class who had to work to support herself, to be responsible for my tuition, food and clothes, everything that cost money. That anger stayed with me even after I got married and ready to have my own family. As I struggled to conceive and then suffered from multiple miscarriages, I also blamed my parents for that because I worked too hard and never had much down time switching from one job to another. Only one day, a day that was very close to my daughter's due date, I made peace with my past and decided to forgive my parents unconditionally. I did that for my child, I told myself. I wanted to gift her the love and presence of her maternal grandparents without the burden of me holding grudges against them.

I still remember the light sensation and the warmth within my body that day after making a promise to myself. I asked the doctor later when they noticed the Hep. B antigens became negative, as apparently they only shared the news after monitoring the blood results for a while. It turned out to be several months after I made that life-changing decision to forgive my very own parents. Based on the metaphysical explanation, anger is the emotion affecting our liver. For years, my liver had been taking in my anger and I suffered from the consequences. Once I was no longer angry and decided to let go, it healed itself.

I've had the honour to meet more people who have had similar stories ever since. Like me, many had become spiritual teachers, meditation guides and life coaches after experiencing the healing power to our physical body by transformational work on our mind and soul. Sometimes when I met my friends who told me about their physical conditions, they often blamed it on age. 'Problems start to surface when you get older'. Yet, when they shared their news and how life had been treating them, I had my answers.

Once, a friend of mine told me about suspicious nodes on her breasts. I did not say anything right away but went on to listen to her rant about problems going on in her life. Then she went on and complained about how she had to do everything for everyone, both at work and at home. No wonder she had ailments with her breasts - she was doing too much 'mothering' and our breasts, a very important symbol of mothers, suffered. Indeed, many women over 40 are at risk of having breast cancer. It was not hard to imagine considering the extent of 'mothering' women have to do at that stage of life. Have you also noticed those around you who are stubborn to the core often have a stiff neck or knee problem? Those are the ones who could not be flexible and never bend their knees!

I then went on to learn Reiki. The healing of my decades-long hepatitis had convinced me that we had the power to heal ourselves as well as others, if we knew how to. That's the reason why there are 'healers'. Doctors are also a kind of healer, as they know how to diagnose and prescribe medicine. Reiki literally meant the healing force of the universe. As energy travels, we have the power to heal by directing its flow. We fall ill when that flow is stuck or blocked, it's that simple. That healing through touches is no news. We all enjoy massages every now and then. We feel relaxed and refreshed after a massage. It's because touch helps restore the natural flow of energy in our body.

A very important ritual - Attunement - is the essence. It is the process when the Reiki master helps his students open up the energy system from the crown, such that they could channel energy more efficiently.

I would never forget my own attunement by my Reiki master, Stephen. The whirling of energy from the top of my head was so overwhelming that I felt dizzy for a while even when the attunement was over. Master Stephen also shared with us that Reiki was intelligent; when we held our hands over something, the Reiki went to where it needed healing. Therefore, he reminded us not to give Reiki when our hands were injured.

The very first person I was told to heal was myself. Master Stephen instructed us to place our hands above twenty-one points of our body, from head to toe, every night before bed for one-and-a-half minutes. As you read up to here, you'll probably think these are all 'hippy' talks. Yet, Reiki is something that you immediately understand after you experience it.

It was so soothing and relaxing that most of the time I fell asleep before having gone through all the energy centers. Even my daughter had given me her endorsement unintentionally. One day not long after my Reiki course, my daughter told me her tummy hurt, so I placed both of my hands on her belly. She claimed she felt much better afterwards. From there onwards, Jasmine asked me to 'hold it' every time she sensed pain in different body parts. It continues to be the first and only thing she asks me to do whenever she hurts herself. In fact, that is the foundation Chinese medicine. Traditional Chinese medicine believes in restoring the normal function of our body, eliminating ailments naturally, known as homeostasis in Western medicine. Especially regarding acupuncture - it applies needles on meridians, or pathways in the body where vital energy flows, to unblock where energy gets stuck. Chinese medicine believes that as energy flows, there is no room for disease to develop further.

If I was not careful I would be like any parents and had my energy drained out of me. I am so grateful that I learnt Reiki and had been attuned to be able to channel energy and draw energy from nature instead of being an isolated magnet and have my energy sucked out by Max's condition.

The key is to tap on the infinite energy surrounding us. The source of vitality from nature is infinite. The energy never runs out. Energy is channelled, flowing from the healer to the receiver, instead of being drawn from one person to another. Learning this gave me a great tip that I did not have to deplete my own energy to care for my sick baby. I could always rely on nature to replenish myself, through meditation and be in touch with nature. I always tried my best to find time to have a walk on our village beach; it was that little piece of paradise that made us decide to move out of the city, to where my father described as 'in the middle of nowhere, once you got here, you don't want to leave but once you'd left, you'd be too lazy to return'. The ocean was the source of my energy, my healing power. Even on days when I could not make it there or weather did not allow, I only had to close my eyes and my visualizations would instantly transport me to the gold sparkles reflected by the waves in the serene sea. Moreover, Reiki could be used along with any other form of therapy, medication, religion, belief system and faith. Reiki could only enhance their efficacy. So every day, I made sure Max and I had plenty of cuddling time. The intelligent Reiki from my palms would travel to wherever healing was needed in his body. I would also express my gratitude's when I was giving him Reiki, as gratitude held immense healing power on its own. In fact, gratitude had the strongest positive power that could lift people up from suffering.

As I was healing my life, I got stuck at certain experiences in the past and did not quite know how to move forward. I even talked about it with Neil as I was clueless about how to resolve it. On that very weekend, my friend Molly, the very same one who came to the hospital and paced outside the operation theatre with me, came to the island I lived on with her visiting friend. She introduced me to Sam, from Brighton. She was very at ease, and I felt comfortable hanging out with her right away and agreed to join them for dinner on the beach. During dinner, she shared with us the special meditation modality she had switched to.

"... because, who has the whole day to meditate?" she reasoned.

She had caught my attention. Who wouldn't want to meditate in the most effective way? Then she told us about Ho'oponopono. As it turned out, this ancient ritual had been my headache I had been having about the unresolved issue - my burden was offloaded.

Ho'oponopono is a Hawaiian practice of reconciliation and forgiveness. The word itself, which is a mouthful, literally means 'double correction'. It corrects, restores and maintains good relationships among family members by getting to the causes and sources of trouble. It believes that we all have a part to play in the problem and we are all capable of also playing our part to resolve it. The meditation often involves affirmations of, 'Sorry, please forgive me, thank you, I love you.' These words expressed at the same time bring compassion, forgiveness, gratitude, and love to us. It is also believed that such practice could cleanse all the negative energy in the surroundings and people in them.

A very famous example is Dr Hew Len who worked as the psychologist at an institution in Hawaii that housed the most dangerous mentally ill criminals. The institution constantly lost its staff. Staff often took sick leave or when they felt brave enough to get to work, they had the habit to walk along the wall to avoid sudden attacks from its residents. Incredible things happened when Dr Hew Len joined the team. Soon, staff ceased to resign, rarely anyone took sick leave, and one day, the whole institution was closed because all the once dangerous residents were well enough to be placed in regular correctional facilities. Yet, Dr Hew Len had never seen any patient in person. Every day he went to work, he took the folders of his 'patients' - and all he did was to do Ho'oponopono meditation.

I was so grateful for Sam to introduce me to Ho'oponopono. I was fascinated by it. I even took a course to study it and became a certified Ho'oponopono practitioner. I understood I always had a part in everything that happened around me. Thus, taking responsibility for my part in everything happening around me, also came the power that I knew I could use to help cleanse and heal it.

At the hospital, we could not help but have this creepy feeling every now and then that gave you goose bumps. After all, it's mostly a sad place where lives passed. Every time when we were admitted, we often found ourselves in a new room - and even in rooms we had stayed in before, it always felt foreign to us again. For a few nights in a row I would do Ho'oponopono meditations. Soon I would feel a serenity return to us. Things became calmer and Max also slept better; it felt more like a second home to us than a cold, isolated oncology ward.

CHAPTER 28

TRANSFORMATIONAL FORGIVENESS

Both Louise Hay, in her workshops, and Jay Shetty in his book, 'Think Like a Monk', talk a lot about forgiveness. While Louise focuses on the healing power of love brought by forgiveness, Jay Shetty gives a more structural explanation on the level of forgiveness.

Obviously, the bottom line is being not forgiving; that is the baseline when you feel the frustrations, hurt and anger brought by this sensation. According to Louise Hay, many of us put ourselves in that prison of unforgiving. Even without the other person knowing, we trap this negative energy within us and worst, recycling it again, again, hurting us emotionally and physically.

The second level is Transactional forgiveness - it is a trade of apologies and forgiveness. It's not bad going through the 'transaction'; negative emotions are released and positive energy is created. A fresh start is given to the relationship between both parties.

The next level is where the magic and healing power lies - the Transformational forgiveness. We forgive without expecting anything in return. There is also a kind of forgiveness known as Unconditional Forgiveness, which is a rare form and is based on a strong foundation of love, such as parents forgiving their children no matter what.

What I would like to talk about more is Transformational Forgiveness, because I have experienced its healing power.

When we know HOW our thinking affects our emotions which then affects how we behave, by changing the way we think, we change ourselves and the world around us, the healing is instant.

I went to do a guided meditative healing session with a very experienced meditator and certified hypnotherapist in order to heal my childhood trauma, once and for all. I was guided to go down the memory lane, back into my childhood days when I experienced all the hurt and insecurity. As my adult self, I soothed that little child and told her everything would be ok. I took that child and placed it in my heart such that I could offer her comfort anytime I needed.

It was an immensely emotional session and is called the 'inner child healing'. We are impacted so much by our childhood and our experiences during the early years become rooted in our subconscious. By healing our inner child, we can heal our old hurts and not let them affect our belief and unconscious behaviours today. We allow ourselves not to relive the experience, but to review it and to revise its impact on us, mentally and emotionally.

We not only have the 'inner child' with us, we also have the 'inner parents' inside. We, ourselves, are often the most critical of ourselves among all. Have you ever found yourself constantly talking yourself down, critiquing and not allowing yourself to become optimistic on certain things, fearing you would fail and disappoint? Didn't all these sound like strict parents who nagged their children to no end without much encouragement? This is our 'inner parents' side. What kind of 'inner parents' would we like for our 'inner child' and our adult self?

Understanding we have both sides was a great healing tool for me. I accepted that's where my vulnerability came from and allowed my inner self to be my biggest cheerleader. I thought of the kind of parenting style we had towards our own children; we naturally leaned towards child-led parenting. Child-led parenting is a parenting style in which you let your children make choices within reason to encourage their independence and personal growth. We were there to make sure to provide a safe and positive environment for them to thrive with guidance but not too much interference such that they could try and figure things out on their own. I decided that I would also apply the same 'inner parenting' style on myself, whether towards myself or my children, because it was based on unconditional love, and for myself, it would be unconditional self-love, here and now.

Chapter 29

Cancer, I Forgive You

Besides doing a short meditation in the morning to start my day, I usually do a proper meditation at sunset to wind down the day, to filter the negative energies and emotions that came to the surface through the hustle and bustle and commotions of the day. It's a great transition to greet the evening with a peace of mind. I also typically end my meditation with forgiveness. I said to the Universe that I'd forgive everyone who had done me 'perceived wrongs'.

One day, I had gone through the same ritual like usual and had forgiven everyone I could think of, including myself. Then suddenly, a picture of what I imagined as cancerous cells came to mind. I was really taken by surprise. I had done my meditation and my mind was in the receiving state for any messages from the Universe.

I took a deep breath and found myself saying, "Cancer, I forgive you," and immediately found tears streaming down my face.

I did not realize how much anger, resentments, and fears I had been holding against cancer. Then I visualized gold sparkles falling upon the ugly, distorted cancer cells - and one by one they turned into healthy, vibrant cells. I remember I playfully added a smiley face on each of them. I knew that then both Max and I were healed.

Chapter 30

The Turning Point

A couple of weeks after my epiphany to forgive cancer, I got a message from my friend Karen, who I met through the local network of parents whose children were diagnosed with brain cancer. Karen was an accomplished and a highly intelligent woman. I knew that she only needed some pointers and she would do all the necessary research and beyond. I mentioned to her previously about the off label drugs we'd read about when researching alternative treatments for cancer, especially for post treatment maintenance; yet, we did not take it far from there because we were waiting for Max to complete his treatment and then bring it up to our oncologist. What Karen told me was about to blow my mind away. But I was not surprised; I knew the transformation of my attitude towards cancer had brought me to that.

Karen had dug into all that she could find on the topic. She urged me to join the Facebook group of Jane Mclleland Off Label Drugs for Cancer. She was the author of the book, 'How to Starve Cancer'*. The theories and suggested treatments explained in detail in her book resonated with me, and in fact, we had been doing 70% of it already - we just needed the rest to complete our regime to help Max to build a stronger foundation and immune system to keep cancer from coming back.

I believe it was no coincidence that I was guided there. I never read or heard any parent in my Medulloblastoma network mention Jane's work. Once I decided to forgive cancer, I looked at the illness from an entirely different perspective. The image of the tumour in my mind when I meditated brought my attention to look at them at a cellular level. How could that few number of cells in the whole entity of our body, which consisted of trillions and trillions of cells, cause such destruction? They were simply outnumbered. Something from the external (of the cells) must have triggered such changes.

Most doctors today still argue about cancer being all genetic. I personally found it hard to believe it. As I was pregnant at a rather late age, we did extensive genetic scanning for the pregnancies of both children, which covered over 99% of the genetic issues. Jane Mclleland's theories and researches had confirmed my intuitions. I signed up for her course and was hungry for everything she had to tell the world.

After watching Mina Bissell's* TED talk* that she posted, about a new understanding of seeing cancer, I was elated. Yes, cancer cells were healthy cells, 'good girls gone bad' as something triggered them, coupled with an unpleasant environment that fused with the evil factors to grow. For the first time in history, scientists such as Mina, were no longer stubbornly focus on the genetics of the cancer cell, but on the micro-environmental factors that triggered a healthy cell to turn malignant, and found out that such a conversion COULD be reversed if we could reset the environment to the right one again.

The conventional cancer treatment is like the old-fashioned way to discipline naughty children - when one child's behaviour is out of line, just go ahead and punish the whole class. That's what teachers at my primary school used to do. They believed that the punishment would teach the naughty one to behave better, while teaching the whole class that if you misbehave, your friends get whipped, too. But then what happened to the misbehaved child? Did he or she become good thereafter? No. From my experience, they became worse. And kids who thought the bad boy looked cool followed suit, while the good ones stayed away. The class became split into good kids, bad kids. Now the teacher had more bad apples to deal with. Each bad apple is a risk to infect a good apple. Imagine the scenario of a cartel. When one is eliminated he is replaced almost immediately. The second-in-command takes over and gathers his soldiers again and strengthens his narcotic kingdom again as long as the environment favours the trade, such as the profit from selling the general public drug.

Not long ago I saw a post on social media from which its members were mostly mothers of different nationalities who lived in Hong Kong. A member posted a question asking why students of the

French International School were 'always standing smoking all sorts of stuff outside their school'. The post received overwhelming responses and comments, and the one that stood out and received the most number of 'Likes' said, 'Such that they would grow up and do the same thing outside Pastis on Wyndham St.' Pastis was a popular hang-out brasserie in the Soho area for French or Francophone residents. The interesting fact was that the majority of young people these days do not associate smoking as cool anymore. I asked my friend whose daughters went to another international school, whether she had the headache of her children smoking. She told me not really, their generation was unlike ours, they actually thought smoking was disgusting and unhealthy. So you wonder, the same generation with likely an equally comfortable upbringing (as international school were considered expensive education here in Hong Kong), and there also was not any evidence showing that the French gene was more likely to smoke compared to other races - so how come many of those students of the French international school were smokers while not the case in the others?

If I am to use Jane McIleland to explain this phenomenon, she would say there are many pathways in the environment that would lead to some becoming smokers while some did not. First of all, there was a rumour that the first time the French International School banned smoking outside the school area, the one that protested most were actually the parents. Hence, we had the parents who first introduced cigarettes into their children's life. Then once they had their own pocket money or managed to get their hands on their first cigarette, they had the taste of the forbidden apple. Realising that is not that forbidden in their culture and within the free time between school and home with little supervision, they smoke more and have more of their friends who might think they look cool and join them - the growth factor. The more they smoke, the more their body becomes addicted to it to the point they find it very hard to live without a smoke or several a day. A bit like once the tumour starts growing, the body's immune system switches off. There you go, you have a growing number of smokers at school who smoke more and more cigarettes.

Of course, if you look at the smoking example, we can easily tell that the best way to stop smoking growing at school is from education. Educate the students about the truth of cigarettes, so that the more students who agree that smoking is bad and uncool, the fewer students would smoke. When fewer students smoke, fewer other students would become smokers. It may even get to a point that these students would go home and tell their parents how bad smoking is. As no more students are smoking in and outside of schools, and fewer parents smoke, the remaining smoking parents are more likely to be frowned upon, so gradually they either quit smoking or quit smoking elsewhere. It is also like in underprivileged neighbourhoods, where all sorts of charity programs are run, such as dance classes, to keep kids off street, from trouble and bad influence. Movies like 'Honey', and 'Steps', all tell the same stories.

During the months of Max's chemotherapy, I learnt more about cancer, and I also witnessed how chemo was eating away at my son. Neil and I often cheered along when nurses set up another bag or needle of poison to be administered intravenously into Max's body.

"Go get the cancer, go kill all of them," we'd cheer.

Yet, as each cycle went by, Max got weaker and it took longer each round for his bone marrow to recover, just to get to the minimum level of blood counts such that he could have another round of chemotherapy again. When it finally came to the last cycle, we rejoiced that it was nearly the end, but we immediately started to worry again - what's going to happen when no chemo is there to kill cancer? By this time, we knew that chemo drugs only killed the tumour cells, but not the stem cells that, in time, would grow bigger and stronger, multiply, and then become the new rounds of tumour cells. What's going to happen to Max? He would not have an army to fight for him anymore, and he had become too weak to fight for himself. Didn't history teach us enough? How many times have big nations flown into a war zone to save the day, bombed the hell out of the place, then left the area weaker and messier? Wasn't the best strategy to train the locals to defend themselves?

It was why it only took a shift for me to entirely change my attitude towards conventional cancer treatments, and look into Jane McLelland's study and other more wholesome approaches. Indeed, although the science was complicated, her principle was simple and easy to understand. It was believed that some changes in our body, such as viral or bacterial infections, left our cells weak and exposed to attack. These attacks caused changes at the cellular level. Then when the micro environment around these cells favour the damage and determination further, then these now 'bad cells' feed on nutrients such as glucose and grow. When they grow to a certain point, they make a leap, and then they become capable of building blood vessels around them to suck in more nutrients that they need and develop their own network to spread. If our immune system is not strong enough to fight it, it will proliferate more, grow bigger and stronger, then become the tumour that makes us pale when we hear its name.

CHAPTER 31

THE AGRICULTURAL REVOLUTION AND CONVENTIONAL CANCER TREATMENTS

In his book 'Sapiens: A Brief History of Humankind', Yuval Noah Harari talks about how the common belief of how the agricultural revolution had changed humankind's history by solving the food shortage problem, actually turned humans towards destruction. The main culprit is wheat. The discovery of such crops had indeed provided answers to the rapid increase of the population on the planet, as well as solving the risk of food shortages, so sapiens could have the peace of mind to advance its species. However, the dependence on a single food source had changed humankind biologically completely. Wheat does not provide us the full spectrum of nutrition humans need, contrary to the various food types humans would have to seek and hunt, if wheat had not been made abundant through agriculture. Wheat also needed lots of pesticide to protect the harvest. As a result, not only is our health compromised, so is our environment and the food chain.

I have similar sentiments towards conventional cancer treatments. The main treatments of cancer are, namely, radiotherapy and chemotherapy. Both therapies target the cancer cells and aim at killing them. Chemotherapy is where toxic chemicals are injected into the body, and let it run through all over and kill cancer cells along the way. Like wheat, they solve the short term problem, or the symptoms, but at the same time weaken the system so much it may as well lead to its own destruction. In fact, chemo drugs originated from mustard gas - the military chemical weapons developed during

World War One. It had been invented to kill enemies, not save lives. Soldiers and cancer patients were used during those days to test the chemical weapons. They found that the chemo drugs offered short term relief for the cancer patients but they did not provide the cure. At the same time, cancer patients suffered horrible toxicity from the drugs and many died from complications, as it still is the case today. I lost count of the number of deaths at the Children's Hospital that were from the complications but not from the cancer itself. And where did the complications come from? Most of the time from the conventional treatments such as chemotherapy that wiped out the patient's immune system and turned their body into a giant magnet of illnesses that would otherwise be minor to a normal person, but killers to them.

On the other hand, radiotherapy uses mainly photon beams or more recently, protons made available to tumour sites to destroy the cancer cells. Patients who have had radiotherapy have a significantly higher chance of developing secondary cancer. The radiation that has been targeted to kill cancer cells, unfortunately, in the case of photon beams, requires an 'exit'. Radiologists can control how the beam gets into the body, but it cannot control how it comes out. It is a lottery whether it comes out somewhere rather harmless or via important internal organs. The half-life nature of the radiotherapy also means that more side effects appear the longer away from when the treatment was done. In the case of brain cancer, I read a lot of stories shared by parents whose children developed cancer or lifelong health issues from the radiation they received at a young age. They seemed to accept it was a price they had to pay for having the children live. But is it really necessary? Cancer treatment seemed to have advanced so little compared to other fields of medicine.

CHAPTER 32

THE UGLY TRUTH OF MEDICINE: MONEY TALKS

Having witnessed first-hand the evil of chemotherapy, I swore and informed my husband that in the very unfortunate scenario that Max relapsed, I would not want to subject him to chemotherapy again, period. Yet, oncologists at the hospital would only administer treatments and prescribe drugs that had been studied under clinical trials. The treatment protocols had to be 'evidence based' and had the statistics to support them. It could not sound more logical and safer. However, there is a big flaw in the system - clinical trials take years and a phenomenal amount of money, and only big pharmaceutical companies or established institutions, who often have the financial connections with large pharmaceutical players, could afford to do so. As a result, only drugs that could make big money would get to the mainstream protocol. No wonder poisonous chemo drugs remain as the cancer patients' 'hope'.

Recently, the Cancer Society in the U.K., has urged their government to make the prescribed drug melatonin to be more accessible to the public, especially to cancer patients. Studies and scientific researches by charities and well-intended physicians have shown that melatonin helps ease the side effects from conventional cancer treatments and in high doses, showed promising results to induce apoptosis of cancer cells. The best part is melatonin costs very little and is natural. It has no toxicity and no long term side effects. Unfortunately, that also means little money can be made from it, hence little support would be given to push for its wider usage. It is the sad fact and ugly truth when it comes to medicine.

A very good example is Vincristine. This was the very first chemo drug that was mentioned to us. Being one of the most common chemo drugs, it was included in Max's initial chemo cycles. However, we found out later that Vincristine was not able to cross the blood brain barrier*, which was essential to treat brain tumours. On the other hand, research had proved that an over the counter drug, Mebendazole, was just as effective as Vincristine in eliminating cancer cells, and it was also able to cross the blood brain barrier. Yet, it only costs about a fraction of the traditional chemo drug. None of our doctors cared about this fact when asked, because they had to follow the protocols that had been in clinical trials and no surprises, mostly sponsored by the big pharmaceutical companies who had an enormous financial stake in the products being evaluated.

When we discussed with our oncologists that we would use natural supplements, off-label drugs and cannabis oil to help Max to detox, protect, strengthen, and eliminate the cancer stem cells, they would not even acknowledge it. We had done our homework on the research and studies, to which they even commented that we knew more than their junior doctors. We understood the pathways needed to be blocked to starve cancers and the synergies drugs and supplements to protect the body from being attacked by cancer again.

We had these contradicting responses from our oncologist:

"Well, if you give Max so many things, you would never know which worked and which didn't."

However, when we asked him which particular pathways and drug we should focus on, his reply was, "You will have to block all pathways, as cancer feeds on everything".

We felt that we never got real support from our doctors. Our goals were not even aligned. We were looking for a cure, while they wanted to buy time. We wanted it all and quality of life for our child. Doctors were only looking at 'survival rates' over the next 12 months. We were not given choices over treatments - it was a 'take it or leave it' and 'one proton fits all' approach. We were not given the choices of hospital either as the Children's Hospital was the only medical institution in the city that would treat paediatric cancer patients.

COVID also made travelling to other countries for medical treatment impossible. These days, we treat Max ourselves, based on what we learnt through online consultations with overseas specialists, and actual case studies from other patients and parents around the world. It was not that we wanted to play doctors; we simply did not want to play the doctors' number game - when they saw Max as one of the many patients, one number on their pie charts. We had been told, even with all the harsh treatments Max had gone through, his survival rate was only 50% and if he relapsed, it dropped to 20%. However, to us parents, it was either 0% or 100%, there was no in between.

Andrew Kaczynski, an investigative reporter at CNN advocated more funding to be injected into the positive curative treatments for paediatric cancer patients. His infant daughter was also struck with the deadly brain cancer. She went through harsh chemotherapy like Max did, which wiped out her immune system and in the end led to her death due to an infection - unfortunately she did not survive the septic shock like Max did. It was a heart-breaking tale that was probably being told occasionally and definitely not enough. He pointed out the very obvious - that the paediatric patient market was simply not large enough to motivate a profit-driven industry, and the medical field to do more very much needed research. It was unimaginable and barbarous to continue to administer chemo drugs, which are literally poisons and military weapons from WWII to our children, without the intention as a curative treatment.

Professor Ben Williams is one of the longest glioblastoma* survivors, the most aggressive form of brain tumour that a patient is usually given fifteen to sixteen months to live even with surgery, radiation and chemotherapy. Then how did he make it beyond that, not to speak of decades beyond an average time frame of survival. Like us, he believed that the conventional cancer treatments would serve only as a temporary answer. For a long term solution, he used a cocktail of non-cancer drugs and supplements to cure his terminal illness. He also pointed out the flaw in the medical system and the challenges of having clinical trials on non-cancer drugs because of the lack of profit in them. Neil and I discussed a lot about such frustrations.

He figured it took on average a decade for a drug to have enough clinical trials and medical data on it for it to become official, to be able to be administered at hospitals. Few parties can spare such expenses except governments and pharmaceutical companies. Pharmaceutical companies, no doubt, only look to their bottom line, but there is little excuse for governments not to invest into treatments that could bring REAL hope to cancer patients. Neil helpfully suggested it could be rather feasible only to use the tax leverage to encourage pharmaceutical companies to invest in drugs that were not at the top of their profitable chart. On the other hand, governments could also use tax rebates to incentivise big corporations to invest in companies who conduct innovative medical research; he even visualised how owning shares by corporations would create healthy cycles of great performance and in return more investments into much needed new approaches towards terminal diseases.

Close to home, many parents questioned why photon beams were still being used in children's radiotherapy. In many developed cities like Taiwan and Singapore, proton radiotherapy was being used as it was much less harmful compared to the traditional photo technology. Photo beams require exits and often cause secondary cancers in other internal organs as results. Sadly, the reason why our government, one with billions of dollars' surplus in each fiscal year, decided not to build a facility that allowed the proton to be available when they built the Children's Hospital, was because of the same reason as the industry who was looking for profits - there was simply not a big enough demand.

It was simply outrageous to learn about something so fundamental, such basic rights for our children, had to be driven by markets.

CHAPTER 33

BIG MANIFESTATION, BIG DREAM

I believe this book will become one of my most important works in life. I even think it's my 'dharma' to get the message out through the telling of my son's journey, in a very positive way.

No parents want to hear that their children have cancer. No parents want to subject their children to any conventional cancer treatments that are available today. Indeed, all parents are terrified to sign their children off to have poisons injected into their bodies or to be radiated. But we are not given any choices. It is outright a crime to force parents to choose between a death sentence or a life sentence for their loved ones.

I would like to ask you readers to help spread the word; send your rockets of desire to the universe. Visualise one day our society being able to provide us with alternatives, curative treatments that will be gentle to the body and strengthen health at the same time, instead of destroying it. Even better, preventative measures put in place so that our children can enjoy the perfect health that they deserve and live their life to the full.

It can definitely be done. There are already pioneer biologists, scientists, and individuals who are trying new things that actually work. I could already name a few if anyone was interested in looking them up.

Care Oncology Centre based in London is a clinic staffed by a team of oncologists and doctors. They believe that standard cancer treatments alone might not be as effective as a combination therapy approach, which will assist in easing the undesirable side effects patients currently have to suffer due to the high toxicity of the chemo drugs. Similar to Jane McLelland's approach, they administer off-label drugs and natural supplements to generate synergies that would enhance conventional cancer treatment, while reducing the side effects through detoxing our bodies and adding on protection for further invasion, while strengthening the immune system as the last defence.

LDN Research Trust, is a charity that raises funds for research trials that studies how naltrexone, when taken in low dosage, assists cancer patients to fight the illness by moderating the immune system. Children with Cancer UK works towards having more research and trials to have more gentle and curative treatments available for young cancer patients. In recent years, they have urged the UK government to make melatonin more accessible and brought forward research showing how this low cost supplement could help cancer patients.

Cannakids, an organisation based in the U.S., believes in the therapeutic power of cannabis, and they help patients who turn to them to understand more on how this medicinal plant could help them. There are also therapeutic nutritional therapies which suggest how cancer patients could have better control of the disease by having a diet that would provide nutrients for healthy, normal cells but not favoured by the cancerous cells.

All these potentials give me hope and allow me to dare to dream. What we need is to have enough small players to convince the major players to come on board, to listen and act soon. It is now up to us to "believe to receive", in order to turn hope into reality, and we need to believe that will happen in our mind first. Never underestimate the big difference that a small person can make.

BIG STEP 6

BELIEVE TO RECEIVE

CHAPTER 34

LAW OF ATTRACTION IN A NUTSHELL

I myself experienced the miracle of healing my long term illness through healing my mind and soul. With my son facing such a terrible disease as brain cancer, I had no idea what I could do. He was born as an innocent, perfect child; there would not be anything within him that resembled resentment, anger, unforgiving, etc. Indeed, children were the most forgiving bunch I had ever met. They fought, they screamed, they stomped their feet, then acted as if nothing had happened after they'd released all their frustrations. So, I questioned, how on earth could children get cancer - some even as soon as they were born? The youngest patient at the Children's Hospital was two and a half months old when she was diagnosed with an aggressive type of brain cancer.

Louise Hay once explained that children who were ill usually had taken on the negative energy from the adults around them. I began to wonder those surrounding Max, including myself, my husband, my daughter and our helpers I recalled how stressed and worked up my husband was from work, or how angry his nanny could be whenever she had a fight with her boyfriend. I stopped myself right there before I let the blame spiral further. I decided to own it up. I must be partially, if not fully, responsible for such a thing to happen in my life, under my watch.

I then became obsessed in learning about the 'Law of Attraction' ever since Max's diagnosis. I wanted to know what part I had played in drawing such an experience into my life. I knew that if I could understand how that worked, I could attract the opposite. I became hopeful that I could help Max to turn things around. I went on to read the series of books on the topic co-authored by Esther Hicks, who taught through the voice of her 'inner being' or 'higher self', Abraham Hicks. I also listened to all her workshops and seminars that I could find on YouTube. The theory was simple, yet very complex. By understanding how the universe worked, you could work it to have everything you ever desired. It sounded like magic but as she explained, you did not have to study gravity to have gravity worked on you. If you ever questioned that, watch a child falling off a tree!! They had not studied gravity, yet they could not defy it.

We all know how radios work. We tune into the station that we want to listen to, then we are able to listen to whatever is being broadcasted through that frequency. In fact, everything is being broadcasted out there. We only have to tune into the right frequency. That's how the 'Law of Attraction' works. When we vibrate at a certain frequency, we can experience everything that matches and vibrates at the same frequency - just like tuning into the desired radio station.

Abraham Hicks has broken down the process into five steps.

The first step was what drove you to begin the process; often it was when you experienced what you did not want. You felt bored in your car, and that led you to turn on the radio. In my case, my not-wanting to have Max suffering from cancer had brought me to the second step: to define what I wanted for him, as if we had to decide what kind of music we would like to listen to on the radio. My desire was very clear, I would like Max to have perfect health.

Hence, to summarize how we could make the 'Law of Attraction' our best friend:

STEP ONE: MANIFESTING
To live your greatest life, you must first become a leader within yourself. Take charge of your life, begin attracting and manifesting all that you desire in life.
- Sonia Ricotti

Manifesting means to be very clear in your mind of what you want. Sometimes it takes some bad experience to realize what you do not want, then you manifest what you do want. Otis Elevator Company was founded by the American industrialist Elisha Graves Otis, who invented the 'elevator' because he did NOT want to use a hoisted platform to clear debris from an abandoned factory. By knowing what he did not want, he manifested what he wanted and that turned into the blueprint of the world's very first 'elevator'.

As Max became medically stable and we focus more on his rehabilitation, I have come to the conclusion that my plan of ever returning to a full-time job, when both Jasmine and Max start school, would never work. Being disabled by the brain surgeries and the side effects he still suffered from the operation as well as his chemotherapy, and he needs intensive care. Yet, I did not want my life just to be that. I believe I could work around Max's needs, to do something for my personal growth, and contribute to my family and the world. A new round of manifestation began.

STEP TWO: DEFINING AND ASKING
The first step is clearly defining what it is you're after, because without knowing that, you'll never get it.
- Halle Berry

'Ask and it is given' - it is the base of the Law of Attraction. Like a computer program, we need to give clear instructions of what we would like it to do for us. When the instructions are clear, it cannot give us anything other than what we ask.

The first time after we learnt about Max's surprisingly stable MRI, after his relapse, Neil and I were overwhelmed with immense gratitude. For the first time since his diagnosis, we enjoyed the very luxury to walk along the long beach near our home, and discuss the days ahead of the family in the longer term, not living for just the next MRI scan. I told Neil that Max's needs would be my first priority, yet I would still like to be able to work part-time, and I would like to be able to combine my passion for creative works with impact - an impact to the environment and to the world. In that regard, we are very aligned. Neil also expressed his wish to be able to do something impactful for his next career move. We felt so hopeful that day, we did not know how all this would happen, but we had no doubt that it was possible.

STEP THREE: BELIEVING

Magic is believing in yourself, if you can do that, you can make anything happen.

- Johann Wolfgang von Goethe

'Believe to receive', is my forever motto. I have had to fight so many doubts during Max's cancer journey, mostly from doctors. They believe their way is the only way. They believe in 'evidence-based' drugs and protocols. However, faith means believing in something before evidence shows. Wasn't it ironic when the doctors asked us to 'have faith in them', when they had not shown any evidence yet to cure my son?

Of course, there is blind faith, as well as informed faith. In the Chinese culture, most regard doctors as God. Most of the parents in our hospital group whose children have brain cancer, believe and follow everything the doctors say to the dot. A lot of the time when I ask them what kind of targeted therapy drugs their children are taking they have no clue. All they know is drug A and drug B. In our case, our belief is that there are treatments other than conventional chemotherapy and radiation work, that has been based on extensive research, experiences and real case studies shared by other cancer patients all around the world.

STEP FOUR: ALLOWING

You clear the resistance, get out of your own way, and allow yourself to naturally receive the things you desire by being in constant touch with your sensuality.

- Lebo Grand

Indeed, we are always our own enemies. We are constantly in our own way to reach our goals. How do we do that? By planting doubts in our head, by thinking that we do not deserve, by running hundreds of scenarios in our head as to why things are not happening or will not go the way we want. Clearing resistance means NOT to do any of those. Doubting ourselves is tiring; constructing unproductive thoughts is exhausting. Why don't we just relax and stop busying ourselves with thoughts that are not helpful?

Since our blissful walk and discussion on the beach, Neil and I carried on with our life and work. We did not think about what we'd discussed too much, although in our heart, we were hopeful. Weeks later, one day, my new neighbour came knocking on the door. She brought some cakes that were leftovers from her husband's birthday party. She also asked me if I knew anyone who had retail and wholesale experiences, as she had some project in mind that she would need to partner with such a person. We sat down and chatted. I gave her lots of advice based on my experiences.

Before she left our house, she asked me, "Would you like to become my partner?"

And so this led to the birth of our business two months later, a sustainability project where I could combine my creativity and make an impact to the environment and the world.

As for Neil, around the same time, a colleague of his had resigned from his company. Hence, his position became open for other employees to apply for. That very position was at the department where his company did all the impact works around the world.

STEP FIVE: APPRECIATING
Gratitude makes sense of our past, brings peace for today, and creates visions for tomorrow.
- Melody Beattie

Do you find yourself not able to stop buying someone gifts, and they are always the one very appreciative of what you give them? The Universe works the same way, too. By being grateful, appreciative for what you get, you create the energy within you and send a message to the universe to give you more. As they say, 'a grateful heart is a magnet for miracles'. It is time to try it out to see what the Universe has in store for us!

Every morning, I listen to Louise Hay's guided morning meditation. I know the words by heart. I still turn it on every morning because I usually have to wake up between 12 and 4am because of Max. He seems to struggle to sleep through the night and peacefully ever since his brain surgeries. I also sleep on the carpeted floor with him as he has the tendency to roll around and climb over things in his half-awake state. Hence we put thick rug down onto the floor and installed cushioned wall panels to protect him. I become his personal guard at night to protect him from hurting himself. As a result, every morning at the crack of dawn, I am exhausted and most of the time, grumpy. The guided meditation reminds me about the plenty trivial things I can be thankful for. Neil cannot stop himself from teasing me every time he walks on me when I have the audio playing.

"Thank you to the kitchen, to the toilet that can flush. Thank you hot shower..." he laughs and then walks away.

It sounds really silly but it does put you into perspective. No matter what is going on in our lives, there are always many things that deserve our gratitude, despite how mundane they can be.

Being grateful puts me into a calm, peaceful space to welcome the day - the day I have never lived before. It excites me and gives me the opportunity to be in awe of what the world going to present to me; the joy and sparkles I witness in my daughter every morning when she wakes up, ready for the day.

CHAPTER 35

EMOTION = ENERGY IN MOTION

Despite the metaphysical theories by Louise Hay being convincing and I myself had experienced the healing power from within, I was determined to find out how the biology actually worked, so that I could prove how the 'Law of Attraction' rules the universe, especially now Max's life was at stake.

DrJoe Dispenza is the author of several international best sellers whose works are about how we can change our reality through changing the way we think. In 'Become Supernatural', my favourite of his books, he interprets in detail what Louise Hay presents in plain English with more complicated, but more convincing scientific and biological facts. First of all, Albert Einstein, the greatest theoretical physicist in history, had already established that all things are energy. Dr Dispenza pointed out that our emotions were basically energy in motion. Such energy in motion generates a charge between our head and sacrum, the energy highway where our seven chakras, the disks or wheels where our energy spin, are located. The charge generates a magnetic force between the two points. Our body then becomes a magnet that draws things, people, and events that spin in the same level of energy. No wonder there was a saying, 'when it rains, it pours'. When we vibrate at a high frequency level, being happy draws more experiences that make you happier. Similarly, when bad luck hits, if we are emotionally affected by it, we will continually draw unhappy events to us.

On the other hand, the neurological fact that our brain cannot distinguish between imagination and reality, we can actually create thoughts in our mind, and the thoughts generate emotions. The emotions trigger energy which draw in various experiences that resonates with that level of energy to us.

When I helped mothers to lose weight, they often admitted the hardest part was diet. Most people believe that losing weight is 80% diet, 20% exercise. Contrary to what people think, most mothers could not commit to exercise; indeed, their everyday life is physically demanding enough. From morning through to the night, it's activity packed. They would blame their struggle with diet on being so tired, they needed comfort food, or in some cases, they felt that it did not matter how much they ate or did not eat, they struggled to get rid of their pregnancy weight. I would tell them they had been looking at it the wrong way. To be naturally slim, it was 90% work in our mind.

I used to believe the same, that diet mattered most, hence I went on to do different detox and diet programs. Yet, few worked. I remember I signed up to do a program called 'Wild Fit', by Eric Edmeade, which claimed it was the only program available out there that married nutritional science with behavioural psychology; by establishing the right relationship with food, you can achieve fitness through transforming your diet. It all sounded very logical. I thought it made much sense until the part that asked me to drop all sugar in my diet. I had never been overweight but I had also never been as slim and toned as I wished. I always had a low carb and low fat diet. My weakness was with sugar - my favourite 'comfort meal' was black coffee with sweets, and I loved sweet and sour candies in particular. To give up sugar was equivalent to asking me to give up a very important pleasure in my life.

Fast forward to Max's cancer journey. We began to look into the Keto diet for him as we read that many cancer patients had benefited from such a diet, as cancer fed on glucose. Neil and I bought a book called 'Keto for Cancer' to learn how it worked, as well as how to calculate the amount of food consumed in order to go into ketosis. In order to make sure the diet was safe, we decided to try the diet on ourselves first. We wanted to see how the diet made us feel and whether it would harm our kidney, liver, or as it happened to one of our friends - affected her thyroid function. The more I learnt about the science of it, I started to believe it could be the answer to many of our ailments. I began to see sugar as the evil source of many physical problems.

During the few months of research, my opinion towards sugar changed; what I used to see as 'pleasure' in my mind, I gradually associated it with 'illness'. Because I knew that I did not want illness, I wanted to have perfect health and great vitality, I began to believe that I could have both when I bid sugar farewell in my life.

So, I went onto a Keto diet with the intention to experiment on myself for Max. I dropped high carbohydrates and processed sugar overnight, and never looked back. I'd paid USD400 to do the 'Wild Fit' program only to stop at the part where we were asked to give up sugar, and yet now, without spending a dollar on any nutritional workshop, I managed to cut sugar out just like that.

I learnt the most important lesson in dieting and weight loss: Our energy level had to be aligned with the food that we wanted ourselves to have. Processed and junk food have very low energy levels while healthy food, which are mostly fresh and organic, vibrate at much higher frequencies. Based on the law of attraction, when you are depressed or emotionally at a low energy level, you are naturally drawn to food vibrating at the same level as you. No wonder 'comfort foods' are often 'junk foods'. Similarly, when your internal energy level is high, you naturally want to be active because that is what you are drawn to. I now found it easier to exercise, even if just for five minutes, than not to exercise on a daily basis. I never have to force myself to work out again. I just want to move - it feels great and as natural as taking a shower or brushing my teeth.

I came to the conclusion that for dieting to work it was not the relationship with food but the relationship with myself.

Money: it seems to most to be the most important thing in life, and many people ask about how we could attract more money. I found the person who gave a very good lecture on money was Marisa Peer, one of the most famous hypnotherapists in the world, because she went straight to the essence of it - that Money is Energy. Back in the beginning when people in different trades began to exchange products, an apple farmer could exchange his apples with the fishermen for his fish. Later on, precious shells were used as a standardized substitute to facilitate the exchange with various sources, on multiple occasions. The 'currency' gradually evolved into today's money, credit, and even digital coins. Hence, we can easily see how money is actually energy. Money flows around such that we can meet the demand of our physical needs. In this sense, if you vibrate at a high energy, you naturally draw in money more abundantly.

Certainly, abundance is not limited to finance - it also includes health, joy, peace, relationships, etc.

CHAPTER 36

ART OF ALLOWING

Argue for your limitations, and sure enough they're yours.
- Richard Bach

Abraham said, "When it is asked, it is given."

Yet, things do not always go that smoothly - why?

We have so many resisting and conflicting thoughts in our head that do not allow us to be in the receiving mode. We ask for more money but then we have thoughts like 'I don't have enough money', 'I am never able to pay all the bills'. If we can master the art of allowing, removing the resisting thoughts, limiting beliefs then we will be in the receiving mode to receive what we ask for. It is the Law of Attraction, it is like gravity, and even if you do not believe it, it is bound to happen.

During Max's treatment, I had many opportunities to put this art of allowing into tests.

Usually four to five days after a round of chemotherapy, Max's immune system would drop to non-existent and enter neutropenia; it was the window when he was most vulnerable to infections. Despite knowing that there was a high chance we would have to re-admit him if fever struck, after a week of being confined in bed or the high chair, we wanted to take Max home to give him a break from the hospital, and to see his darling sister.

A fever could be a reaction to chemo or to the drop of neutrophils, but we would not know for sure until tests were carried out to rule out the chance of infection. Before that, we were instructed to take Max back to the hospital so that antibiotics could be administered right away. After the third cycle, we took Max home as usual, praying that he would not get a fever - but he did. We managed to keep him home for about thirty-six hours; thirty-six hours of bliss and joy before we had to rush back to the hospital. As no one was expecting him, no room with baby facilities had been reserved for us.

The ward we got put in was next to the one we just checked out of two days before. It was a room designed for older kids. It was cold, freezing cold, with central air blowing in your face. There was no tall standing bath so with Max's condition, it was impossible to bathe him. And not bathing him increased the chance of developing skin infection. Yet, I was still very grateful that we had an isolated ward to protect him from possible further infections. I made a silent wish, wishing that we could move to a baby ward. I made my wish but did not think much of it afterwards. I focused on caring for Max. Two hours later, I heard a crack. I turned to the direction of the sound and saw something incredible unfolding in front of my eyes - there was a large crack in the centre of the glass window of the patient ward. There was no major movement that would have caused such a crack.

At the first sight of it, I was alarmed about Max's safety, so I quickly pressed the Help button. A ward assistant was asked to check on us. Upon approaching the room, she saw what was going on and ran away immediately to get help. Seconds later, the intercom by the bed was on. A nurse asked us to have the curtain closed around the bed and stay put. They would send the maintenance team over.

I followed the instructions but left a gap open - I wanted to keep my eyes on the cracking situation because I had never witnessed such things before. It was like being in an earthquake movie. The crack moved and travelled in all directions to the four corners of the window. Within minutes, there were cracks everywhere. Two technicians arrived and they did not dare to approach. They stood at a distance away and watched, too. Then all of a sudden, numerous cracks appeared on the glass window, then 'bang', the whole window shattered into tiny pieces fell all over the floor.

Once the drama was over, the contractors quickly and efficiently cleared the glasses, and once the debris was cleared, the nurses urged us to pack up and be ready to be moved. Knowing the ward was busy, I expected to be relocated to the general ward, which was not ideal as it was even more challenging to look after Max there. Then, to my surprise, we were moved back to the ward where we stayed during chemotherapy. The room was still occupied that morning but the patient was discharged an hour before the window incident and had been cleaned and sanitized. It was a whirlwind of packing and moving. Once we settled down, we had the visit of the department head who came to make sure that we were ok. The hospital took it seriously, as such things had never happened before. To date, this was still the most unbelievable law of attraction coincidence that I have ever experienced.

CHAPTER 37

REMOVING LIMITING BELIEFS

Before 1954, the common belief was it was not physically possible to run a mile in less than four minutes - until a man, his name was Peter Snell, did it, just a few seconds shy from four minutes. Since then, many people have done it, and gone beyond what everyone thought impossible for a very long time. This was probably one of the most famous stories to show us what was POSSIBLE when we remove our limiting beliefs.

I am a believer of that. Indeed, my career was built in travel retail. I worked for many years for luxury brands to develop and manage their markets in the traveling sector like the airports. Our motto was. 'The Sky is the Limit', which to us it meant literally as such. Although that was my previous life more than a decade ago, I still carry the same spirit in me in life. It helped me to go beyond something that had been coded in my subconscious mind a long time ago.

Here's a very simple example, which probably resonates with many. I struggled with food for a very long time. I had the tendency to finish whatever was served on my plate. I had the urge to finish all of it. This resulted in an overeating habit. How did that happen? One day, as I was finishing a family size packet of crisps and my belly was threatening to burst, I still found myself eating until the last piece was shoved into my mouth. I was shocked and felt sick. Then it dawned on me that when I was small, I was told by the adults that I MUST eat everything on my plate or in my bowl. They kept retelling the old myth of how many grains of rice we left in our bowl would be the number of spots our future husband would have on his face. When you grew up listening to stories like 'Beauty and the Beast', that was the last thing you would wish for yourself! And the other tactic used to make me eat everything on my plate, was being told how hard farmers worked to grow our rice, and how children in Africa had no food. All these had submersed in my subconscious mind in order to make me finish everything. It was incredible how that had become my belief and been controlling my eating habit for so many years. I ate quickly, a habit that I still need to remind myself to slow down, and cleared absolutely everything. I was not able to do otherwise, until one day I realized the source of such a limiting belief and removed it, literally, overnight. Now, I would not think twice if I had to leave a bit of food behind, because not finishing the food would not cause a child somewhere in a poverty-stricken area to starve to death. And eating food that my body did not need was the same as wasting food. And guess what, I could always box them up and eat them again when my body was hungry again.

Such limiting beliefs have also been shown to affect how people look at their health by the medical history of other family members. Angelina Jolie made a drastic decision to remove both of her breasts because many women from her family got breast cancer, and she had undergone some tests that showed she was more prone to have it. Her limiting belief had led her to do such a shocking preventive measure to herself. What if she had gone beyond that, and thought instead, "It happened to many of my ancestors, but it did not have to be the same for me. We now have a lot of research to show how we can pay better attention to breast health and prevent it from happening?"

Indeed, from the extensive research that we have done on cancer ever since Max's diagnosis, we came across lots of studies on breast cancer, and there were so many things we could do and take to keep them healthy.

When our doctors told us that even despite the harsh treatments Max had gone through, his survival rate was only 50%, again, their statistics created many limiting beliefs for patients and their loved ones. However, when it comes to your own survival rate or your loved one, there can only be either 0% or 100% - and the choice is easy to make - 100%, and we decided we better start believing that we could go for that, now, and stop letting the limiting belief hold us back.

BIG STEP 7

LIVE HAPPILY EVER AFTER

CHAPTER 38

WHAT IS HAPPINESS TO US?

Living happily ever after seems to be the 'end game' for most people. But first, we need to define what happiness is: Is it being rich? Being successful? Being beautiful?

Happiness depends on the correlation between objective conditions and subjective expectations.

People are made happy by one thing and one thing only — pleasant sensations in their bodies - a reaction to various hormones coursing through their bloodstream, and to the storm of electric signals flashing between different parts of their brain.

The road to happiness is a complicated journey. For most the road seems long, windy, and is always under construction. They think that they can only be happy when they land certain jobs, find the Mr or Mrs Right, have a certain amount of money in their bank accounts, or when they have certain materialist fulfilment. However, there is always a shortcut if we know how to get onto it.

Before that, however, we probably need to define what real happiness is, and I wanted to be happy even when my son is battling cancer.

Based on the above, if my happiness depends on external conditions, on Max's progress, my happiness would always depend on something I cannot control. In other words, the cruel reality is, I will always be unhappy. Even if I feel happy by Max's improvement, the happiness will only be short term.

True happiness can only be seeded, nourished, and grown from within. No external circumstances can do anything to help if we do not do any internal work to groom it. If we want our plant of happiness's to grow, we first need to take the initiative to do the groundwork and plant the seed. Then we have to clear the weeds, water it on a daily basis, and give it fertilizer when needed. Similarly, we need to do the groundwork and plant the seed, and recognize we are responsible for our own happiness. Then clear negative thoughts and self-doubts, as they are just like the undesired weed taking away the nutrients and space from the soil for our happiness plant to grow. Then we need to think thoughts of joy daily as the much needed water for the happy plant to grow. And we need to regularly give ourselves a pat on the back, self-approval, and praise as fertilizer as a boost to our happiness plant to grow tall and strong.

CHAPTER 39

FLEXIBILITY AND MIND GYM

On the first day of my belly binding course, the very first handout we were given was not any teaching materials related to the course. We were each given a card of 'Character Value', on which the print said:

FLEXIBILITY
Definition: 'Adjusting to change with a good attitude'
With Five I WILL:
1. Anticipate change
2. Adjust when needed
3. Look for the benefits
4. Finish the job
5. Do what is right
The card ended with two quotes:
"Flexibility is actually key to stability."
"If you can't be flexible in life, you become irritable in life."

It was meant to remind us that when we work with mothers, it was essential to have such an attitude because despite the intention to help the mother relax and recover from childbirth, her priority was still on the baby, so we had to keep that in mind and be ready to accommodate with last minute changes. I have been keeping that card close to my heart ever since, as it not only reminds me to have the capacity to be flexible with my clients, I have found the wisdom to be very applicable in life in general.

As Louise Hay emphasized - A flexible body is more comfortable to live with, similarly, a flexible mind makes life more comfortable to live in.

Life is full of changes. A life without changes is dull and boring. Stress is actually fear of change. Therefore, when we are flexible and embrace the changes in life, we won't have stress. We can finally enjoy the adventure life brings us.

How do we develop a flexible mind then?

I dedicate a relatively big portion of my yoga classes to practice meditation with my students, because as mentioned above a flexible mind is as important as a supple body. Sometimes students do not think they've got the best value out of the class if they were not doing asanas all the way till the end. So I came up with what I call 'the Mind Gym', to give an impression that could resonate to them. My mind gym is composed of three parts.

PART I. MEDITATION & ART OF BREATHING

Those who have never tried meditation often think it is just 'think nothing, and focus on breathing'. This is very right but also very wrong. Meditation, in my opinion, is our gateway to turn inward, such that we can allow our inner wisdom and messages from the universe flow to us. We have the answers to all our questions and problems if we can quieten our mind enough to listen to our inner voice. However, we are often too busy thinking, what they called having a 'monkey mind', to allow that to happen. A 'monkey mind' is similar to a highway blocked by traffic gridlock. It is not hard to imagine people who find themselves on such highways - they are angry, frustrated, irritated, and often cannot find their way out - they are 'stuck'. When we meditate, our goal is to free that traffic and turn our mind into a country road with an idyllic flow of vehicles every now and then. We do not stop any thoughts but allow thoughts to come into our mind. We acknowledge their coming and going and we can see what they are because the traffic is low and slow enough for us to do so. That way, we can catch the inspirations when they head our way.

The most common and best technique to meditate is, indeed, to focus on our breath. Not only slowing and deepening our breaths calm us down and clear our head by bringing in more oxygen and relaxing our nervous system, our breaths also follow us wherever we go. If we use our breath as our anchor, we can meditate anywhere and at any time. We can survive hours without water and days without food, but we won't survive minutes without air. Focusing on our breathing also reminds us to trust life because our most precious breath's will always be with us.

Think of our heart as like the CEO, our mind the COO, and our body the executives. Meditation is like our CEO meeting with our COO. Once the COO (brain) gets the right instructions from the CEO (heart), the executives (body) follow through. It is that simple. According to scientific research, there are 40,000 sensor neutrons relaying information to the brain from the heart. The heart pumps blood 100,000 times a day to all the organs of the body, and communicates to the brain and the body through the nervous system connections, the hormones produced in the heart itself, biomechanics information via blood pressure waves, and the energetic information from strong electrical and electromagnetic fields. Indeed, the electromagnetic field of our heart is 100,000 times stronger than our brain. That explains how people who are declared brain dead are still alive because their hearts are still beating.

We all breathe but we do not quite know how. Until I learnt about breathing properly, I had been breathing rather involuntarily. Learning the art of breathing was eye-opening as well as life changing for me. If you are interested in learning about the science and art of breathing, especially on nose breathing, I highly recommend the book 'Breath: The New Science of a Lost Art'* by James Nestor.

Growing up I used to have very serious hay fever. I sneezed from the moment I woke up. It was so bad that it affected how I functioned on a day to day basis. However, when I started to practice yoga, my yoga instructor constantly reminded us to breathe through our noses. Breathing through my nose helped fix my hay fever allergy. Our nose simply has the right features to filter and moisturize the air before it enters our body. When I was at school, my classmates used to tease me that I could never 'shut my mouth'. My congestion was so bad that my mouth was forever slightly open to help me breathe. Days after I began to breathe through my nose, my mouth naturally closed and it improved my overall appearance as my protruding front teeth gradually adjusted themselves as well. I no longer needed them to shift forward to enlarge my mouth interior to let me gasp in more air!

According to James's book, many people who suffer respiratory problems and apnoea benefit much, some even have health issues permanently eliminated without surgeries or medication, simply by breathing correctly. The book was fascinating; it even covered how the internal structure of our nose resembles that of our sex organs - men do not even need Viagra if they can master the art of breathing!

PART II. NEGATIVE BELIEF CLEARING

Negative thoughts are often rooted from negative beliefs. Thoughts such as 'I will never be rich' can come from negative beliefs about money. When I was little, the adults around me often made comments like 'rich people are greedy', 'money stinks'. So, if your subconscious mind associates 'money' or 'wealth' with 'ugly' and 'evil', why would you think they would come to you when you have already rejected them in your mind?

Of course, negative beliefs are not easy to get rid of if we do not know how. After all, they are patterns of thoughts that have been developed and accumulated throughout the years, some from our very early childhoods. I was convinced that with a childhood like mine, I must have hoarded mountains of negative beliefs within me, so I decided to take a course and learn the powerful technique of asking the right questions in which the answers would help me in clearing out any negative beliefs, step by step. Here is the snapshot of how you can take a few simple steps to help you get going.

First, we need to identify these negative, limiting beliefs. We can do so by simply checking what is NOT working in our lives. How are you doing with relationships, career, finance, etc.? If you think you are 'stuck' somewhere, there's often a negative or limiting belief somewhere that stops you from moving further. So, we locate when and where it started so you can uncover it. We can always rely on our sensory system to recall that from our memory. Have you ever heard a song that reminds you of a certain person, a certain period of time, or a certain event? Does a scent, a fragrance or even a foul smell take you down the moment lane? These things generate emotions within us and our senses often work as a connection between those events that caused such emotions. It's almost like a file in a computer; once you click open, all the contents and data are right in front of you again.

What is the negative, limiting belief?

When did you start believing it?

How did that make you feel?

Do you really believe that?

What would you rather believe?

How does that make you feel now?

The above are simple yet powerful steps and questions that help us eliminate and re-establish some new, and unlimiting beliefs that will bring in positive emotions and impacts to our life.

PART III. VISUALIZATION: CONSTRUCT YOUR OWN LIFE MOVIE
A negative mind will never give you a positive life.
- Paulette Carlyle

Dr Joe Dispenza pointed out that if we did not train our mind on positive thinking, it would be easy to predict we will go through our lives in cycles of similar events; that's when we describe that we never seemed to 'get a break?' Why is that?

Think about when you first get up in the morning. Do you often grab your phone right away, check your messages or emails as soon as you have turned off your alarm? And did you do just the same the night before as you turned in? When we go through all these 'data' and 'memories', they generate 'thoughts' which in turn, create 'emotions' within us. Then these emotions draw in events that create more of the same emotions to us, as they are vibrating at the same energy level. As a result, we live in a similar pattern of reality.

Hence, a quick morning meditation can help us to break out from the pattern of creating the same negative events in our lives. All we need to do is to visualize a great new day, that in return generates great feelings within us. The positive energy simply draws positive events for the day. It is that simple.

Visualization is one of the most powerful tools and effective ways to train our mind. Think of it as a virtual 'gym' for our mind. Unlike the realistic gym that makes us sweat and our muscles sore, this virtual mind gym is fun, wild, and enjoyable. There are people who build a whole business just on helping their clients to construct their mind movie. People are willing to pay because they work. With my belly binding clients, from Day One, I told them from now on, every time you picture yourself in your mind, visualize the version of you that you desire - the body type, the look, and the feeling.

The drill of regular training of my mind has been the key to how I coped and stayed sane throughout Max's cancer journey. My heart and my mind had become my shelter whenever I felt the world was crumbling down on me.

CHAPTER 40

GREATEST TEACHERS IN OUR LIFE

If you think you are too small to make a difference, try sleeping with a mosquito.
- Dalai Lama

Every one of us can be a teacher. In fact, everyone around us can be our teachers. When a student is ready, the teacher will be there. It only matters whether we have an open mind and heart, and are willing to learn.

Louise Hay talked a lot about family. She had a traumatic childhood and like me, she had done a lot of healing before becoming the great teacher she was. According to her, we chose our parents because they were perfect for us, for the lessons we came to learn in this life. In a similar manner, we are connected with our children at the soul level. We are always mistaken that our job as parents is to teach our children but in fact, they come to teach us what we need to learn in our life. Our children are, in fact, our greatest teachers.

We all think that it's our parents' job to teach our children about life so they can become independent and can contribute to society. I only came to understand it's actually the other way round now that I am a parent.

The biggest lesson my firstborn taught me was to never settle for second best.

Jasmine is beautiful. She is a happy, bouncing five-year-old who only wants the best for herself. I had repeated miscarriages before she was born. It had been some depressing, dark days for me, but now looking back at the other end of the tunnel, I can imagine

Jasmine scanning and screening all the embryos until she found the best to settle with. She was stunning even as a new-born. I never found new-borns endearing, most of them looked like some crumbled skin to me, but not Jasmine, and not because she's my daughter. I actually have pictures that my husband took of her when she was still laying in the incubator. She is smiling in every single one of them. I had never seen such a symmetrical face in a person. Her eyes sparkle and dance whenever she talks. And how she loves dancing. She could dance freestyle to any music and you become just mesmerized by her.

She is also the funniest girl I know. I called her the 'CEO', Chief Entertainment Officer, in the family. The most precious thing to us is how sweet and caring she is towards her brother. Even when Max had all his hair, eyebrows, and eyelashes fall off due to chemo, and he looked pale and weak, Jasmine still thought her baby brother was the cutest thing in the world.

Neil and I agreed that she was the best therapeutic treatment for Max. We could not wait to get him home from each inpatient stay. After each of Max's chemo cycles, we knew that within a day or two we would have to bring him back to the hospital because he would have entered neutropenia and a fever would spike, either from infection or just a reaction to high doses of chemo. Yet, despite knowing we would only have a couple of days at home, we would go through the hassles; pack up everything and take him home. The effect of his sister on him was incredible. Max was like a new person, no actually he was his old self, when he's home and with his darling sister. While physiotherapists had to use toys and tricks to incentivize him to move, he naturally crawled up and down and followed his sister around.

During the early days when Max could barely move except his head, we spent lots of time sitting by his hospital crib reading to him. I gathered all the stories he loved, especially the Peppa Pig series. When we got bored of reading the same stories over and again, I went to look for new books; I wanted to find something morale boosting, more for us than him, in fact.

I came across the series about Max the cat. I got the book titled 'Max the Brave' right away. Max the cat wanted his peers and the adults to see him as a brave cat, and he knew that a brave cat caught mice. So he went on an adventure and asked every single animal he ran into whether it was a mouse, so that he could catch it, because he had no idea of what a mouse looked like.

I could not find another better story to describe our very own Max the Brave: He had no idea what a giant monster he had to fight and the ordeal he had to go through on a daily basis. Yet, day after day he demonstrated his bravery and unbeatable will to live. He never complained or cried through the chemo cycles which we could only imagine how painful and uncomfortable it must have made him feel. He needed injections on a daily basis into his thighs. I tried to alternate each day, after horrible chemo drugs went through his body for a week, in order to help his bone marrow to recover sooner. His thighs were bruised yet he took in everyday without a flinch. He was, according to the nurses, the only child in the WHOLE hospital who would take medicine by himself. Nurses would put his medicine in syringes, then I would transfer it into a little cup, then place the cup in front of him. The nurses always asked if they needed water and other things to help him take the medicine, then one day they had their mouths dropped open when they witnessed Max take the syringe one by one, and push the syrup or mixed solutions into his mouth. We were so proud of him.

He wanted to have fun and play every day and even managed to make funny faces himself in his attempt to make us laugh at him, because he found it so funny. His attitude had given me so much hope because I asked myself, someone with the will to live and enjoy life as much as Max did, deserved and would live a very long, happy life. I never had a hero figure in my life, not even those superheroes in cartoons and movies as I knew they were all fantasies, until I gave birth to one.

Every relationship in our life is a reflection of yourself, as Louise Hay pointed out. Some reflect the positive side of us, while some reflect the opposite. Very often, people who irritate us the most are the ones who came to our life to teach us the most important lesson about ourselves. I agree with her as keeping this in mind helped me not to be angry with anyone anymore. Whenever I react to something that someone says, I know that it is time for me to reflect and learn, and I say a silent thank you to that person. It does not mean that we have to tolerate others' misbehaviours. Forgiving others does not mean we have to condone what they have done to us. It simply means we are willing to let go, and not to give away our power and let them or the event affect us.

CHAPTER 41

GOOD DAYS, BAD DAYS

Even after making transformational progress in our journey of co-existing with cancer, and I have gained much inner peace, I still have days that things do not go very smoothly; sometimes all go very wrong.

Max has severe PFS, Posterior Fossa Syndrome, which affects his walking, speech, sleep, and his emotions. He has been put on rehabilitation training ever since his discharge from ICU. From being able to just move his head, totally mute, and unable to swallow after his brain surgeries, he has made a huge improvement. He can now walk with assistance, has fine motor skills close to his peers, and makes himself comprehensive with some help with mummy's translation.

Yet, we struggle to get him to sleep better and have a better control of his emotions. Many of the children who have brain ailments suffer from insomnia. When Max's tumour was removed, the void where the tumour used to be remained hollow. In other words, there is always a void that cannot be filled; hence many pathways have been broken. He vomited a lot. I knew that it had affected certain pathways as well as his brain surgeries. We had a 'puke bowl' ready at the dining table, in his play area, and by his bed. He was too young to give us any warning if he had to purge. If we were lucky, we managed to get a bowl in front of him just as he gagged, while at other times it meant we had to change him, ourselves, and clean the crime scene. I have lost count of the number of times when he just vomited, projectile, into my face. Sometimes I even thought it's in my imagination that I could smell the puke even on days he was fine. Only recently, we learnt from other parents that

Max actually has frequent heartburns, which sometimes result in his 'morning sickness'. Since he cannot express himself properly, we have to do investigative works. His MRI scan assures us that he is medically fine, hence we reverse back and study the time of day he vomits, and the food he has the evening before.

Even with a high dosage of melatonin, it is a rare occasion for Max to have a restful and peaceful sleep. On top of that, his little body remembers all the trauma it has been through and is often releasing it during the sleeping cycle. Nearly every night, Max constantly jolts up and flaps around like salmon, putting me on alert 24/7. I have since moved to sleep with him at night to prevent him from hurting himself banging around during the night. We have cushioned the bedroom which he shares with his sister but he still manages to find somewhere every now to give himself a bruise on his head or eye. As a result, I cannot recall the last time I slept through the night. I feel like I have never left the new-born phase, given my son was born less than two years after my daughter, then he was diagnosed when he was eighteen-months-old. Lacking enough sleep and rest, I can easily become ornery on a bad day.

So, what do I do? I have trained myself to focus on the thing, even if just only one, that goes well. Yes, you are right, it's easier said than done. I had the same reaction when I first learnt about that technique, especially when shit rains. But the fact is, it works. For example, on days when my daughter is particularly difficult, I remind myself things about her that are so adorable, even if it is the same thing I have to remind myself of everyday. It's like the story or joke my husband keeps telling people, even when his audience gets bored, he feels good telling it. Speaking of the value of getting out of it! In this digital age, it gets easier when you have stored so many funny videos of your children. An easy way is to KEEP WATCHING THEM UNTIL YOU FEEL OK. When you begin to pay attention to one good thing, it becomes easier to be drawn to another, then another.

And don't forget to ask and ACCEPT the offers of help. COVID hit us in full force a month after Max's diagnosis. Our parents were simply not in the position to help us. However, we were offered help to bring food to the hospital for us, toys and books that keep Max occupied and Jasmine entertained. Babysitting for our daughter was done by our neighbours. Prayers, hundreds of prayers by my mother's church, our friend Justin's church in England and many more by meditating friends, were offered. We said 'yes' to everyone and accepted with gratitude. The truth is, some of our friends who were too stunned or did not know what to say or how to react to our dire situation, still wanted to help. And sometimes you can tell them how they can help. I had no doubt they would come running to give us a hand. My husband told me how his willingness to show his vulnerability to his team during this difficult time had earned him much help from them; how they stepped up and took more responsibilities at work. Indeed, it also showed my husband that to be a good leader is also having the capability to display his human side, to seek help.

These days, after my morning yoga, I spend a few minutes meditating. During the night the tension in my muscles are activated, so I need to clear my mind and instil serenity. To do this, I close my eyes and picture the anchor of my inner being, the radiating sea of our village beach. I feel the connection and love from it. I place my palms on my heart and make a mental promise:

I promise to enjoy this new day.
I go through the day with gratitude, compassion, and
appreciation.
May my day be filled with joy and happiness.
May I always react with love.

Gabrielle Bernstein is often criticized for copying and re-quoting other teachers' works. Yet, I think she has done a brilliant job to summarize and to re-create affirmations that are easy to remember and apply. My favourite which I use to end my morning ritual is,

I forgive my past,
I release the future,
I honour the today and now.

Such practice has worked wonders so far. Bad days always end up being not-so-bad-at-all days.

CHAPTER 42

FOCUS ON THE WELLNESS, NOT ILLNESS

My daughter Jasmine only sees her baby brother's wellness.

Almost every single day, she says "Oh, Max is so cute. He is the cutest boy in the world."

She would say this even over the months when Max had no hair, and his beautiful, long and curly eyelashes were gone, and the disappearance of his eyebrow completed his look of a cancer patient.

She knew that there was a monster in her baby brother's brain which was why he had to spend so much time at the hospital and take either mummy or daddy away with him. Yet, whenever Max was back home during breaks between his rounds of chemotherapy, she behaved towards him and treated him as if nothing had happened. I realized one very important thing - she only saw wellness in her baby brother, not illness.

It was the same for Max. He did not see himself unwell. All he wanted to do was to play and follow his sister around, despite everything affecting him being physical. He did not get emotional nor take it personal with his condition. I often found this ignorance of his was bliss. I could focus my energy on his practical needs, although looking after a sick child who is at toddler age is no joke.

I recently came across something called the Brain Injury Card, on which it stated the symptoms of a brain injury that would help strangers to understand the person's need in case assistance is required:

- Poor coordination, balance, or muscle control
- Blurred speech, vision, or impaired hearing

- Difficulty with attention, concentration, memory or understanding
- Difficulty controlling anger and/or aggressive behaviour
- Confusion, disorientation, dizziness
- Difficulty processing and slow response time
- Impatience, anxiety, or agitation
- Seizures headaches, or fatigue

Except for seizures, Max displayed all the other symptoms on a daily basis. I am not talking about ignorance here and pretend his problems do not exist because they are right in front of my eyes. And we as his caretakers have to be ready and know how to respond according to his needs. These are our actions or activities in our everyday life; the same as we brush our teeth before bedtime. What I would like to say is we can choose the area to focus our emotions on. You would not think twice or have any feeling triggered within you by the need of cleaning your teeth. These days, I do not think twice when I have to stay alert whenever Max moves around as he has severe ataxia; as my daughter describes Max being "very wobbly". I do not get emotional and cry over the fact that Max's friends run around while Max has to be carried everywhere he goes.

It does take practice to train your mind to focus on the good things as we react to events as much as we need to act. Give yourself time and be kind to yourself. If all else fails, brainwashing always works. Affirm many times, as many as needed, throughout the day; 'focus on the wellness, focus on the good' and 'all is well, my children are safe', until it sinks into your subconscious mind so that it comes back to remind you whenever you are in doubt.

CHAPTER 43

FINDING THE NEW BALANCE

When it is dark enough, you can see the stars.
- Ralph Waldo Emerson

Don't judge the moment, turning sufferings into manifestation, look for the silver linings. Pick the words or phrases you like. The point is very simple - when you stop being bitter about the hand you have been dealt with, you will find ways to enjoy the ride and make the best of it. Look for the shining stars in the dark, but if you focus on the darkness and complain how you cannot see clearly, you miss the beauty and the radiance from the stars.

***

Since children were not allowed into the ward, my husband and I struggled to have someone watch our daughter while we did our handover at the hospital. Our neighbours had been very kind to offer play dates to Jasmine but after a while, we felt that we somehow neglected her and were too dependent on outside help. I searched for things to do around the hospital to see what we could do with her to include her more in our 'hospital outings'. I found an ice skating rink near the Children's Hospital. I would have never thought of it if we were not in the vicinity of it.

I got quite excited and I found some figure skating videos on YouTube and showed them to Jasmine. I asked whether she wanted to learn ice-skating. I told her she could have lessons somewhere close to the hospital and she was over the moon. Her ice skating lessons become the buffer hour for my husband and I to do the handover and swap shifts between our son and daughter. Most importantly, Jasmine loved her new found hobby, and she developed much confidence being able to balance on a blade. Indeed, she thought she knew how to ice skate already. "Push, push, glide", Jasmine mimicked Peppa Pig.

Even after Max completed his chemo, we tried to do the same during our regular blood check. Due to COVID however, the ice skating rink had been closed. Ringo, Jasmine's ice skating instructor, suggested to me to get a pair of roller blading shoes, so the rollerblade shoes were the Christmas presents we got from Father Christmas that year. I decided to get myself a pair, too, so it could become a mother-daughter thing to do together. So at the age of 40, I found myself learning to rollerblade with a four-year-old. My husband also took skateboarding lessons from our neighbour's teenage son, (he thought rollerblading was not manly enough for him).

I love our new family activity. In spirit, we are all learning our new balance, together with Max, until he can walk without aid. The courage I saw in Max also encouraged me to take the stand up paddling board that had been sitting idle in the house ever since Neil got it for me for our anniversary down to the beach. I would never have thought or dreamt of doing either stand up paddling or roller skating in a regular year, least of all in the year of chaos. I was grateful for being able to embrace new adventures. Thank you for the gift of being in awe with life again.

Five months after the completion of his chemo treatment, Max unfortunately had a very bad blood infection from his port line. He was not in a state that needed to be hospitalized but he did need to have strong antibiotics intravenously around the clock. Our home was a one-and-a-half-hour commute from the Children's Hospital so the doctors said we would be better off staying as an inpatient. However, staying at the hospital was not an option for us anymore. His brain injury made him restless at night and we felt that the sleeping arrangement at the hospital was not safe for him anymore. In fact, the night after his surgery to remove the port line, the nurses had to tie him up in his crib such that he would not bang his head around in the iron crib. It broke my heart to have to do that but we had to put his safety first. It was also very boring for Max as he felt well enough to play and wanted to move around. The hospital environment was not child proof and all hard floors, which meant Max would be confined in his high chair again. So, we did not have the heart to do that to him again. In the end, we decided to make it a family 'staycation' and stayed at a hotel that was only a fifteen-minute drive to the hospital. We also got a good deal courtesy of COVID. We had not had a holiday for more than a year, so that was it. We had a great time away from home.

**

Studying our biology at the cellular level helped me understand cancer better, and a pleasant surprise was that I also came across studies and possibly answers to the key of longevity and anti-aging. I learnt that it is possible to live a very long life, and be healthy until the day we die. Lots of theories and preventions of aging overlap with that of cancer.

It is in fact quite basic - our cells are unable to repair themselves. So, what causes that, and how can we change that? As Dr David Sinclair wrote in his book 'Lifespan', it is possible and easy to reverse that. The preventive measures can save governments billions of dollars, give humanity more years to thrive, and ease the pressure to reproduce within the biological time frame. I absolutely agree, and love the idea of taking the initiative to prevent problems created by aging, then tackle all the ailments brought on by aging when it is too late. Our current medical ideology is limited to 'killing diseases', instead of 'building a stronger body', and is simply outdated. Entering my forties, I cannot ask for a better gift for myself than the gift of youth.

When I was pregnant with my two children, because I'd endured multiple miscarriages, I was always worried that something would go wrong. After they were born, I then worried about them getting hurt; I almost wanted to put them back into my belly, to protect them. Having the experience of learning how to process all these unproductive thoughts swimming in my mind, I finally built the inner confidence and peace I needed - I could trust the process of life. I am grateful for this gift of peace.

Most of all, the love that is getting stronger by the day. As Louise Hay reminded us; love is not a substance, it will never run out. Love is rather like a muscle, the more we use and train it, the stronger it gets. Love is a gift that keeps giving, and I am eternally grateful for the gift of forever love.

CHAPTER 44

HOW TO HELP

I added this chapter after reading a long, angry, and sad post from a fellow parent whose child also suffered from the same kind of brain cancer as Max. Being much older and at school, the mother complained about how her daughter had lost all her friends during her cancer treatment. The same sad fate also fell upon her. Worse, her best friend cut all contact with her in the past few years, when she needed her most. Her ex-best friend reached out only recently to apologise, and explained that she simply did not know what to do nor what to say. But by then it was too late - their friendship was permanently damaged.

This post had received overwhelming responses. Everyone agreed that they felt the same, but could not pinpoint what it was. Then, what one mother said was so 'on point'. She said, "most people say and do things to make themselves feel well, not the other way round."

So, if you are reading this book, not because of you yourself or a loved one are battling cancer, and you have managed to read this far, I have the confidence to conclude that you have the compassion and desire to help, if cancer, the universe forbids, one day knocks on the door of someone you know.

Gathering most the parents in our group together, we agreed that the biggest help we could hope for was practical help: preparing meals, arranging carpools, running errands, doing grocery, babysitting, helping with housework... really what we need are basic, practical stuff that any busy, time poor parents face and would appreciate the help with. Besides being time poor, many also struggle financially. Medical bills and reduced income because having to care for the sick child creates a tremendous financial burden on families that have been struck with cancer.

There was a mother who was constantly crying for help on social media. I felt for her. The father of her two young boys was in jail and she had to give up her job in order to look after her cancer child. Her family reluctantly took in her older one during the cancer treatment in another state, but as soon as the treatment was over, they passed the other child back to her again. Her sick child, like Max, was still weak from the chemotherapy and suffered from posterior fossa syndrome. She received no sympathy from her family who thought once the treatment was done, it was just like before as if she had two perfectly healthy children. The demand from her two sons made it impossible for her to work. She almost wished her child was back in the hospital, because at least there the meals were provided for and they could receive the little subsidy they were eligible for. Out of the hospital, she found herself drained, physically, mentally, and financially. One day I read she did not even have the gas money to drive her sick son to his check-up. Several parents, including myself, sent her small amounts of help via PayPal. This mother struggled all the way until the very end. Even after the passing of her son, she had to do a fundraising event to raise money for the funeral.

There are endless heart-breaking stories like this, courtesy of Mr. Cancer, of course. Therefore, if you see someone having a crowdfunding campaign in order to get through cancer, donate as you can, without any judgement. The need is real and most of the time, urgent. Do not avoid your friends or families, either. If you don't know what to say, tell them the truth but also tell them you are thinking of them and you are willing to help, if they can let you know how. If you live very far away, send them a card, or even an email or a text to ask about them. Tell them to take as much time as they want to reply. Do not force an update. Sometimes we are simply exhausted by the day's events, or we are still processing the situation. Give us time, and time will tell. Prayers and positive thoughts are almost always welcome. It does not matter what religion you have or which God you believe all roads lead to Rome. All prayers bring healing power. We take any, and all of them.

To summarize, whichever side you are on, be kind and be brave. I found these two very principles took us very far. It was the biggest lesson from the fairy tale 'Cinderella'. Although it's been controversial in recent years regarding the sexism in these classic Disney stories, there are still timeless wisdoms from these simple children fantasies that we could all learn from. If we ever walk a mile in another's' shoes, we would understand why they behave the way they do. Kindness matters and whatever you give out returns to you multiplied. And if you are ever on the receiving end and fighting the cancer war, be brave, and enjoy the thrills from the ups and downs of the ride - there is a light at the end of each tunnel. And most importantly, be kind to yourself.

Chapter 45

Making Peace with Death

You can never lose your loved ones, as you have never owned them.
- Louise Hay

When Max was still treading the water in his high dose chemotherapy with stem cell rescue, one of the dogs of a playdate of Jasmine passed away. Coincidentally, the name of the deceased dog was also Max.

One morning she said to me, "Mummy, Max died."

My heart gave a lurch. I felt a pain in my chest, wondering whether Jasmine could feel something I could not, and something bad had happened in the hours since I'd left Max at the hospital and come home to see his sister. Reminding myself to react with love, I took a deep breath.

"Darling, please don't say things like this," I said to her. "Max is doing very well. He was playing with his car when I left him this morning."

Jasmine then went on to correct me and explain that it was the old dog of her friend, Mackenzie, who had passed away a week ago.

Sighing a huge relief, I went on to tell her how sorry I was to hear such news and whether she had given her friend a big hug. Once we confirmed her friend was actually doing alright, albeit a bit sad and missing her dog, Jasmine began to bombard me with questions about death.

She had many questions regarding death, mostly the usual, "why do we die", "where do we go to after we die?", "Can we not die?", etc. Yet her biggest concern about being dead, was not what we, or I myself, would usually associate with it - the pain, agony during the process, and losing everything you love, or worse, being unable to be where I want to be and do things that I love anymore. Jasmine's worry was singular, that she would not be able to see mummy, daddy, and her brother again. And she was also very concerned about us being dead. To her, mummy and daddy, despite still young in age in our own minds, seemed ancient to her. We were so 'old' in her eyes that she was certain that just like her friend's dog Max, we would die soon because of our 'old age'. Finally, and fortunately, Jasmine let the subject subside after I reassured her that both mummy and daddy would live millions of years more, and I would tell 'the lady in the sky' to arrange us to be in the same family again in our next lives. She seemed very pleased with the answer and I thought it was so sweet that this was the solution of what bothered her over the subject of 'death'.

After this serious conversation with my daughter, I dug deeper into the topic inside my own head. Indeed, growing up my thoughts and feelings toward death were always associated with pain and fear. When I was a child, I always wondered what would be the least painful way to die. I thought of ways that people died: I'd heard that people who jumped off from the top of a building would be similar to a watermelon dropped from a height. Ewww, what a horrible and disgusting scene. People who were caught in a fire and could not escape, oh it must be like burning in hell. Car accidents, oh no, I once saw a teenager who had his foot exposed in a hospital from a car accident, and if that was just an injury, it definitely would not be the way I would like to depart this world. Finally, I settled on carbon monoxide; it seemed to be the most 'romantic' way to go, you simply passed out and you died peacefully with rosy cheeks. I prayed to go that way, or in my sleep, as some described an old person did in newspapers. Whatever happened when they took their last breaths, they always mentioned how peaceful they looked.

Once I'd grown up, I did not really think much about death, as I was so busy making a living - I focused on 'to live'. It was only after I married and my husband and I vowed to stay with each other, until death do us part, did we get down to the business of preparing a will. We then updated our will when we had our first child, to arrange guardianship and put our assets aside, and wrote statements of wishes of how we would like our children to be brought up. I have to say, writing a will, was a very good exercise to understand how we see and feel about death. Indeed, I was no longer worried about the pain, I was more concerned about the pain my death would put onto my husband, my children, and in summary, my loved ones. In the worst case scenario, if both my husband and I died, and our children survived us, they would no longer have their parents to protect them - that became my fear of death.

Never had I thought that I would have to ponder otherwise, that my children would go before me. The moment Max was pushed into the operation theatre for the first time to remove the tumour in his brain, I kept rephrasing in my mind, as if he could hear it, even under general anesthesia, to beg him not to leave us, we're not ready to let him go. Please stay alive.

Now, after taking his hand in mine and sharing his journey with him, learning, growing and healing myself, I choose to trust in the process of life. Max's journey was not only for him but also a journey for me to learn and to heal. I thank him for giving me this opportunity to learn more about myself, my purpose in life, and benefit from more healing. I choose to believe that it's also Max's journey he's meant to experience in his life. He has had his own lessons to learn and he has chosen me as his mother, as I was perfect for him and to guide him through, help him live his life to the full, for as long as he shall live. He has come to this life to love and be loved. Louise Hay once said, 'when we die, the only thing we can take with us is our capacity to love.' I can not think of another boy that has been loved more, who also gives his unconditional love in return.

When Max's oncologists informed us that they saw signs of a relapse from his MRT scan, the same fear of losing him engulfed me again. It took me a whole weekend to process and tone down the fear, and finally make peace with it. If - if the end of his cancer journey was not remission but the opposite, I knew that I would not be losing him, as I had never owned him. He was his own person and had his own path to take; only his was shorter than ours. I would miss him though, terribly. I could take thousands of photos and videos of him, to record his face, his laughter and voice, but I would forever miss his amazing baby scent, the touch of his cheek on my face, the grip of his tiny fingers on mine, the weight and warmth of his body when he used mine as his bed...

I also went onto Facebook to the group page where parents whose children relapsed asked questions. I posted a question and asked those who had lost their children to brain cancer, what it was like towards the end. Was it painful to them? What did they do to ease that pain? What did they do to help them depart in a comfortable way? What did they wish they had done differently?

Based on the collective answers and comments, I made my mind up that I will not subject him to more harsh treatments. Instead, we focus on his quality of life. We make every day like his birthday as indeed, we are celebrating every single day that he is alive and well. We make memories that one day will make us laugh, instead of make us cry. We take every opportunity to tell him how much we love him and how immensely proud we are of him.

I am glad that my daughter ambushed me with such a topic and shared with me her opinions on 'death'. My heart melted when she told me to make sure to arrange us to be in the same family again. That day, I had a private conversation with the lady in the sky, the Universe, that if they had to take Max away from us, I would now like to request and wish to arrange us in the same family again, so I could spend another lifetime loving him, and cherishing him.

Every Saturday afternoon, the Mobile Library visits our village for several hours. It is a truck with shelves of books lining the interior. We can request books online in advance and the truck delivers or we can just choose from books that it carries. Jasmine loves exploring in the Mobile Library. We are allowed to borrow a maximum of eight books at a time. She is always more interested in those books than the ones we have at home, not because they are more interesting, but because she knows she only has them until it's time to return the books.

So, don't you think we should have the same attitude towards life? If we see every day as borrowed, we would never take life for granted. We would treasure our time, our loved ones, live our life to the fullest, and enjoy everything, each moment as if there's no tomorrow.

I once read an interesting article about what dying people thought they regretted most, and not surprisingly, many of them shared similar regrets at the moment when their life was slipping away. Here is the summary:

I wish I had spent more time with the people I love.
I wish I had worried less.
I wish I had forgiven more.
I wish I had stood up for myself.
I wish I had lived my own life.
I wish I had been more honest.
I wish I had worked less.
I wish I had cared less about what other people think.
I wish I had lived up to my full potential.
I wish I had faced my fears.
I wish I had stopped chasing the wrong things.
I wish I'd lived more in the moment.

It seems that dying people, the most honest people, agreed with what I have shared in this book. There is, in fact, no other way to live, for anything else is not living.

The only things you can take with you when you leave this world are the things you've packed inside your heart.
- Susan Gale

What would you like to have packed in your heart when you leave this world? Regrets, anger, guilt, resentment? Or peace, joy, gratitude and love?

THE END

'Cancer, I Forgive You' Meditation

(You can actually substitute 'cancer' with other physical conditions, and even any circumstantial conditions. The impact of the outcome is equally powerful.)

Preparation: find a comfortable and private spot to sit down, close your eyes and begin to breathe deeply, and slowly. Slow and deep breaths help us to relax and allow us to go within easier.

> I forgive you cancer.
> I value the lesson you brought me and my personal growth from it.
> I make peace with your arrival, presence and departure.
> You can now release all anger, resentment, guilt, blame and fear within you and me.
> You can lovingly let go.
>
> I imagine you to turn into golden, radiant and healthy cells.
> You no longer need to turn yourself malignant for your energy is now forever changed to positive.
> Love is the most healing force there is,
> and forgiveness is the way to love.
> And as I forgive you, you are forever healed.

Then visualize a gold and pink light illuminate from within the patient. Feel the warmth from your slow and deep breath circulating through your body, and imagine this healing warmth running through the patient, too.

I understand it is no easier task. Of course, how can it be? To many, cancer is a cold-blooded murderer, a home wrecker who breaks marriages and tears a family apart. It is a parasite that never seems to leave the host. If you take cancer to any court, no doubt the judge would find it guilty, no jury required. It deserves the capital penalty. In short, it is simply unforgivable.

Even when you find it hard within yourself to forgive cancer, and your anger and hatred for it has gone too deep at the moment, it will still work. All you need to do is to be WILLING to do it. If you cannot bring yourself to begin it with 'cancer, I forgive you', you can say instead:

"I recognize that I have much anger and hate within me towards
(*the condition*),
I want to let it go.
I am willing to try and make peace with it."

Then continue with the visualization as described.

AFTERWORD

At the time of publishing, Max is medically stable. He relapsed two months after finishing his intensive chemotherapy which involved stem cell transplants. We were utterly shocked and heart-broken. Our oncologist urged us to sign on for radiation therapy for Max, but we opted for quality of life. He was so happy at home, after spending most of the previous ten months at the Children's Hospital.

Neil wanted to get him onto a low dose chemo protocol to extend his days for as long as possible. I refused and we got into arguments. I believed the actions out of fear would never work. During the ten months while Max was undergoing conventional treatments, I had the chance to go outside the box and do research on alternative treatments. These treatments had many case studies and scientific research to support them. Only, no pharmaceutical companies saw these treatments as profitable enough to sponsor decades-long clinical trials, a requirement to get into the hospitals for patients in need.

We reinforced and introduced more agents, a combination of supplements, off-label drugs, and cannabinoid oils to create the synergies to support his immune system, induce apoptosis of cancerous cells and protect Max from viral infections. His following scan showed stability without further progression, then his next scan after showed the cancer cells were diminishing. Our doctors had no words. After all, they did not give Max much time to live and urged us to talk to psychologists to prepare for the worst and his last days.

I am not certain of what worked. I believe it was everything combined - the synergies of everything we gave Max and the prayers he had received from friends and families all over the world, the Reiki healing I religiously gave him every night after he went to sleep, my faith that he would live to an old age with a great life ahead of him, or simply because of his bravery, his indestructible will to live...In the end, it did not really matter - I could not be more grateful to be able to embrace him, kiss him, and continue to hold his hand in this challenging journey together, for another brand new day.

As for myself, I gave up the plan to return to work full-time when both my children reached the age of school. Still, I believe I can have it all. I can look after my family, while at the same time do something for financial gain, my personal growth and joy. COVID, in a way, became a big blessing in disguise for my situation. The past twenty months have proved that it is possible to work from home. Since six months ago, I began to invest more time and effort into developing my online business as well as my life coaching career, because now it is acceptable and technically possible for me to work remotely as well as anywhere I want, as long as there is Wifi. Compared to Glenys, my editor, who faced similar challenges with her daughter years ago, I am much more fortunate. Not long ago, we still lived in a world in which employers believed their employees would only do their job properly if they sat in the office in front of their desks. Glenys did not have the luxury to both look after her daughter while still making an income. For that, I am very thankful for how time has changed, to make things easier for me.

Neil and I are currently hooked by the Netflix medical drama series, The Good Doctor. It follows Dr Shaun Murphy, an autistic surgeon with savant syndrome and a troubled past who moved from Wyoming to work at a prestigious hospital in California. It is not hard for the audience to imagine the challenges Shaun would face considering the complexity at a social level when dealing with his colleagues and patients. I would have not watched such a show just a few years back because I would have found it too depressing. These days, however, it brings me joy and comfort to see how Shaun thrives and increases in his awareness and understanding of the social interactions with other people. It is unsettling to have a glimpse of the challenges Max is likely to face growing up, but it does give me hope to hope, to dream that Max can go beyond 'average' and 'normal'. He can excel in what he does, and have something to teach the world with his kindness and bravery.

I would like to finish the book with the poem shared with me by my beloved editor:

IT COULDN'T BE DONE

By Edgar Albert Guest

Somebody said that it couldn't be done
But he with a chuckle replied
That "maybe it couldn't," but he would be one
Who wouldn't say so till he'd tried
So he buckled right in with the trace of a grin on his face.
If he worried he hid it.
He started to sing as he tackled the thing
That couldn't be done, and he did it!

Somebody scoffed: "Oh, you'll never do that;
At least no one ever has done it;"
But he took off his coat and he took off his hat
And the first thing we knew he'd begun it.
With a life of his chin and a bit of a grin,
Without any doubting or quiddit,
He started to sing as he tackled the thing
That couldn't be done, and he did it.

There are thousands to tell you it cannot be done,
There are thousands to prophesy failure,
There are thousands to point out to you one by one,
The dangers that wait to assail you.
But just buckle in with a bit of a grin,
Just take off your coat and go to it;
Just start in to sing as you tackle the thing
That "cannot be done," and you'll do it.

Glossary

Abraham Hicks – the 'non-physical entities' of the world-known American channelled and inspirational speaker Esther Hicks. When Esther goes into her meditative state and receives words and wisdom that flow into her mind, she credits those to be the teachings of Abraham and she as his channel and interpreter. More available on www.Abraham-hicks.com

Law of Attraction (7 book series) –

'The Vortex: Where the Law of Attraction Assembles All Cooperative Relationships'

'Money, and the Law of Attraction: Learning to Attract Wealth, Health, and Happiness'

'Manifest Your Desires: 365 Ways to Make Your Dream a Reality'

'The Astonishing Power of Emotions: Let Your Feelings Be Your Guide'

'The Law of Attraction: The Basics of the Teachings of Abraham'

'The Amazing Power of Deliberate Intent: Living the Art of Allowing'

'Ask and It is Given: Learning to Manifest Your Desires'

All co-authored by Esther Hicks and her late husband, Jerry Hicks.

Blood Brain Barrier – a membrane that acts as a barrier between intracranial fluid and external toxins or pathogens in order to protect the brain from having infections, while allowing nutrients to reach the brain. It is made up of endothelial cells and is highly selective. In order to treat a brain tumour, it is essential that certain drugs are able to pass through the BBB to be effective.

Cannakids – Cannkids is an organisation founded by mums whose children were diagnosed with cancer but hoped to have more wholesome treatments for their kids. They believe we do not have to kill the body at the same time eliminating cancer cells. They turned to the medicinal plant of cannabis. More is available about this in the Netflix documentary, 'Weed The People', and www.cannakids.org

Children Cancer Foundation - A charity in Hong Kong, founded more than thirty years ago, to provide caring services for the families of paediatric cancer patients. More available on www.ccf.org.hk

Facebook pages that may have helpful to cancer patients or their caretakers:
> Always Hope Cancer Protocol Support Group (Private Group)
> Jane McLelland Off Label Drugs for Cancer (Private Group)
> Relapse Medulloblastoma (Private Group)
> Mindful Cancer Parents (Private Group)
> C.K.C. (Private Group)
> Max Love Project (Charitable Organisation Page)
> Cannakids (Personal Blog)

Glioblastoma – also known as glioblastoma multiforme (GBM), is the most aggressive type of brain cancer. The average survival time is 12-18 months, with only 25% surviving more than one year and 5% more than five years. The most famous survivor of GBM is American Sandy Hillburn who was a 11-year survivor as of 2017. She participated in a clinical trial that targeted to build her immune system to attack the cancer cells.

Golden Space – A Singapore-based holistic wellness and mediation centre with locations in other countries. More information available at www.thegoldenspace.sg

Head Start 4/IV – preceded by Headstart I, Headstart II and Headstart III, is a study of a different regimens of induction and consolidation chemotherapy for children who are too young to receive radiation. It typically consists of five cycles of induction chemotherapy that involves chemo drugs Vincristine, Cisplatin, Cyclophosphamide, and Methotrexate. Then usually followed by one to three cycles of high dose chemo drugs of carboplatin and etoposide. The difference of Headstart IV from its predecessors was the flexibility in deciding between one and three stem cell rescue conditions with high dose chemo depending on the responses to the induction cycles or risks of initial diagnosis.

High dose Melatonin – Melatonin is a neurotransmitter-like compound derived primarily from the pineal gland. There has been research on the therapeutic effects of high dose melatonin on cancer, especially the hormones involved in cancers such as breast cancer. In 2018 at their International Scientific Conference, Children with Cancer UK invited leading international experts to present how cancer patients could benefit from taking melatonin, especially as a complementary therapy to lighten the side effects from conventional cancer treatments. More available at www.childrenwithcancer.org.uk

Jane McLelland – a chartered physiotherapist as well as four times survivor of lung cancer. She authored the book, 'How to Starve Cancer' which details the science behind and the metro map on how it is possible to block the pathways that enable cancer to grow and thrive. Many cancer patients have success in trying her protocol, with or without receiving conventional treatments. More available at www.howtostarvecancer.co

Jay Shetty – British born Indian, educated in the UK then went onto become a monk at an ashram in India. He found his 'dharma' or calling and has become a transformational author of the book, 'Think Like a Monk', and hosts his own popular podcast show, 'On Purpose'.

Keto for Cancer – written by nutritionist Miriam Kalamian who had lost her son to brain cancer, dedicated her life to look for therapeutic diets for cancer patients. Her most important work, 'Keto for Cancer', acts as an important guide for those who would like to integrate a ketogenic diet as a lifestyle change or as a complementary therapy for health purposes. The book fills the void of the lack of such nutritional guides in the market that explains the science behind how cancer patients can benefit from a ketogenic diet and how they can approach such a diet.

Law of Attraction (7 book series) –
'The Vortex: Where the Law of Attraction Assembles All Cooperative Relationships'
'Money, and the Law of Attraction: Learning to Attract Wealth, Health, and   Happiness'
'Manifest Your Desires: 365 Ways to Make Your Dream a Reality'
'The Astonishing Power of Emotions: Let Your Feelings Be Your Guide'
'The Law of Attraction: The Basics of the Teachings of Abraham'
'The Amazing Power of Deliberate Intent: Living the Art of Allowing'
'Ask and It is Given: Learning to Manifest Your Desires'
All co-authored by Esther Hicks and her late husband, Jerry Hicks.

LDN Research Trust – A UK- founded charity whose aim is to initiate clinical trials of Low Dose Naltrexone for autoimmune diseases and cancers. It is believed that Naltrexone, when taken in low doses, can act as an antagonist and reduce inflammation and the speed of unwanted cells growing. More available at www.ldnresearchtrust.org

Louise Hay – Full Name Louise Lynn Hay, the late American motivational author of the sensational best-selling book 'You Can Heal Your Life' and transformational speaker. She was also the founder of Hay House, a publisher of mainly self-help books. More information available at www.louisehay.com

Medulloblastoma – one of the most common types of brain cancer in children. It is usually a solid tumour around the lower back part of the brain or near the cerebellum, hence often affects the child on coordination, balance and movement. In the case of metastasis, the cancer spreads to the spine along the CSF (cerebrospinal fluid). There are mainly four subtypes of Medulloblastoma, namely, WNT, SHH, Group 3 and Group 4. With WNT having the best prognosis and highest survival rate (>80%), and Group 3 the worst prognosis with survival rate about 50% or lower, Max's subtype was Group 3. The standard treatments of Medulloblastoma include radiation and chemotherapy.

Mina Bissell – Mina J. Bissell is an Iranian-American biologist in her eighties. She dedicated her career to the role of the cellular microenvironment in cancer which has become one of the most important directions of where therapeutic cancer treatment should head. She has received many awards that recognize her contribution in the field of cancer research. Her famous and influential TED talk was presented in June 2012 which is available on the YouTube channel TED titled: Mina Bissell: Experiments that point to a new understanding of cancer.

Parents of Children with Medulloblastoma – A private group on Facebook where members are mainly parents or close families of children who have been diagnosed with Medulloblastoma. Practical information and experiences are shared. New members also seek emotional support from other members who have been through or are still surviving the journey.

Posterior Fossa Syndrome – also called cerebellum mutism, a common complication from post-surgery that is required to remove a tumour in the region of posterior fossa inside the brain. It often affects the patient's speech (where the mutism description comes from), balance and mobility. While mutism in speech is usually transient and usually comes back in time, the other conditions take a longer time to recover and often even result in life time challenges to the affected.

Proton radiation – also known as proton beam therapy, is a rather recent radiation technology that applies a proton beam instead of the traditional photon x-rays or gamma rays as a form of therapeutic treatment for cancers. The advantage of proton therapy versus its photon counterpart is its ability to focus or narrow further on cancerous cells with minimal damage to neighbouring healthy or normal cells. Furthermore, proton beams, unlike photon rays, do not require an exit hence minimising unexpected damage to internal organs.

TED Talks – talk and conference events organized by TED Conferences LLC (Technology, Entertainment, Design), an American Media Organization that posts talks online for free distribution under the slogan, 'Ideas Worth Spreading'. TED Talks are being held nowadays all over the world, with renowned speakers in all fields.

The Fault in Our Stars – a novel-based movie launched in 2014. The novel was of the same title written by John Green. The story evolved around two teenage cancer patients chasing after a fantasy to find out the true ending of a novel on a girl who was also a cancer patient similar to them, they travelled all the way to Amsterdam, during which romance between the two teenagers unfolded.

Acknowledgements

Dr Fanny Lam, Specialist in Developmental-Behavioural Paediatrics, the only doctor who agreed with me that Max needed a MRI to have his brain checked out. Thanks to her swift decision and arrangement, the majority of Max's tumour was removed within twenty-four-hours after seeing her for the first time.

Dr K T Liu, Specialist in Paediatric Neurology, Dr Lam's colleague who took over from her once we had Max's MRI scan. We were floored by his sympathetic bedside manner and his continuous follow-up visits and asking about Max even after handing over our son to the public hospital system.

Dr Wilson Ho, the best brain surgeon in the city, for operating on Max two hours after his admission, and in between his shifts at the hospital. Thank you for gathering your dream team, bringing them to come and talk to us to give us confidence when Max had to go back into the operation theatre a second time within three days, after we nearly lost him the first time round. Fellow parents never cease to sing your praises whenever your name is mentioned. I am always in awe by all the admiring stares from nurses and other medical staff in your presence at the hospital. You are always the first one to deliver the news and reports to us parents even before our oncologists have time to go through them.

Dr Kevin Cheng, thank you for successfully regulating Max's intracranial fluid and avoiding the need to put in a shunt. I enjoyed watching you roll out your tools when you removed Max's stitching. I could tell that performing a surgery is like an art to you!

Dr Carrie Wong, Dr L. C. Wong, Dr Anderson Tsang, Dr Vincent Lam, Dr Ilya Carl, Dr C. H. Ho from the Queen Mary Hospital, you are the unsung heroes behind the scene in the operation theatre. I had to go through Max's medical reports to find out who you were. Thank you for being an indispensable part of Dr Ho's dream team to make the surgeries successful.

Nurses in the Paediatric ICU Ward of Queen Mary's Hospital, for looking after Max intensively for one month in between and after his brain surgeries. Thank you for being kind and empathetic to us parents and always trying to accommodate our requests whenever possible.

Dr Dennis Ku, our oncologist at the Hong Kong Children's Hospital, for always willing to sit down and listen to our concerns. We are grateful to have you leading Max's case.

Professor. Geoffrey Chen, Department Head of Oncology at the Hong Kong Children's Hospital, for making yourself available to us in times of need.

Nurses and medical assistants of Stem Cell Transplant (Ward 5E) and Oncology (Ward 5W), thank you for looking after us and tolerating us parents during Max's inpatient days.

Doctors from the Stem Cell Transplant team, especially Dr Pamela Lee and Dr Noelle Ngai, thank you for being kind and supportive during those three months of Max's critical treatment.

Miss Ada, Clinical Psychologist at the Hong Kong Children's Hospital, thank you for bringing sparkles in Max's eyes with your energetic play therapies and your green frog.

Occupational therapists at the Hong Kong Children's Hospital, especially Helen, you made our life a lot easier and bearable with all your help and visits to Max. Thank you for believing in Max.

Speech therapists at the Hong Kong Children's Hospital, especially Yoyo, and physiotherapists at the Hong Kong Children's Hospital, especially Pat, Carrie, and Joyce. I mention the two departments together as you are the ones who make an effort to personalise the patients' preference. Thank you for bringing all the toys that Max liked to wow him during your sessions with him.

Karen Tang, my fellow mother whose son is also battling with brain cancer. Trusting myself to reach out to you brought me much help and support from you, and a dear friend. I wish Jack to grow up healthy and live a long, happy life, just like Max.

Brenda Tsang, a registered and experienced physiotherapist and my dear childhood friend, thank you for coming all the way to do home visits to help Max to get on his feet again. Thank you for your enthusiasm and simply being a supportive friend.

Arnold Lam, my father, who was the first person I called after learning about Max's diagnosis. I felt like the little girl again and wanted him to have my back. He did not disappoint. He has been with us every step of the way and gone out of his way and beyond to help us, support us, and give us space when needed.

Jacqueline Kwok, my mother and her husband Uncle Rocky, for gathering all the church members to pray for Max throughout the battle with cancer.

Sandie and Edward Johnson, my parents-in-law, for flying here to help us with our daughter while we had to be by Max's bedside when he was in the ICU. Thank you for starting on all that research when we were still trying to accept what had happened. It led to a good start for us to do further investigations and be our son's advocate.

Melanie, Jackie and Michael, our helpers of many years who are like families, who were our indispensable help throughout Max's cancer journey. We could not have done that without them. Especially aunty Melanie, our helper, who has been there since Max was born. Thanks for your love and patience for Max and being an essential member of the caring team for Max.

Vinci Au, my childhood friend who is known to us as Sandy. Her father was fighting against cancer at the same time. Thank you for understanding the emotions I was going through and most importantly, encouraging me to write this book.

Molly Grenham, a dear friend from my mama's club. Thank you for always being there in the heat of everything. Thank you for pacing outside the operation theatre with me during those nerve wrecking brain surgeries that lasted for six to seven hours.

'Mother Tereza', a fellow mother whose son Joseph was Max's neighbour during his ICU days at the Queen Mary Hospital. Thank you for setting a fine example of love and inner strength at times when I doubted myself, if I had what it took in a mother to be the pillar of support for my son. May Joseph rest in peace, and peace continue to warm your heart until the day you met him in heaven again.

Miss Lorraine and Fanny Mama, who were Max's teachers at his play school, and took care of their students as if they were their own children. Thank you for the most welcome visits to the hospitals before the hell of COVID let loose. Your voices of book reading brought much comfort and joy to Max. Thank you for being my Chinese medicine consultant (Miss Lorraine's father and husband of Fanny Mama is a registered Chinese medicine practitioner). The Chinese medicine that you recommended me to give to my children has opened my eyes and mind to the importance of strengthening our immune system to stay healthy, versus the conventional way to treat diseases, of attacking the culprits.

Glenys, my editor, who had been my trusted genie to bring sparkles to my books since my very first one. She was the co-editor of my first book under the pen name Orchid Bloom, and I never looked back and looked for another editor. I hope this book was more exciting than the weather almanac she's been working on.

Jasmine, my daughter and Max's darling sister, who was my greatest teacher and the one who taught me to focus on Max's wellness instead of illness. Jasmine adores Max who lives to come home to see his sister again. Indeed, in her eyes, her brother was totally healthy despite what we told her about the monster in his head. She treated him as such and inspired me to do the same. Thank you for being an absolute bundle of joy and the CEO (Chief Entertainment Officer) in the family with your wits and crazy dance moves.

Neil, my husband and Max's beloved daddy, who is an amazing partner and a dedicated father to his family. I simply could not have done it without you.

Last but not least, Max. You are the bravest boy I know. Your resilience and humour humbles us. I have never had a hero figure in my life until you came along. I wish you a long, healthy, happy and fulfilling life. Mummy and daddy are immensely proud of you. We love you to the moon and back.

About The Author

Shirley Johnson is a life coach, yoga instructor, wellness therapist, a product designer, and a writer. She also writes under the pen name Orchid Bloom. Shirley loves creating and helping people to heal. When she is not doing either, she enjoys life with her friends and family. She lives in Hong Kong with her husband and her two lovely children. She can be reached by email at: lifecoachshirleyjohnson@gmail.com